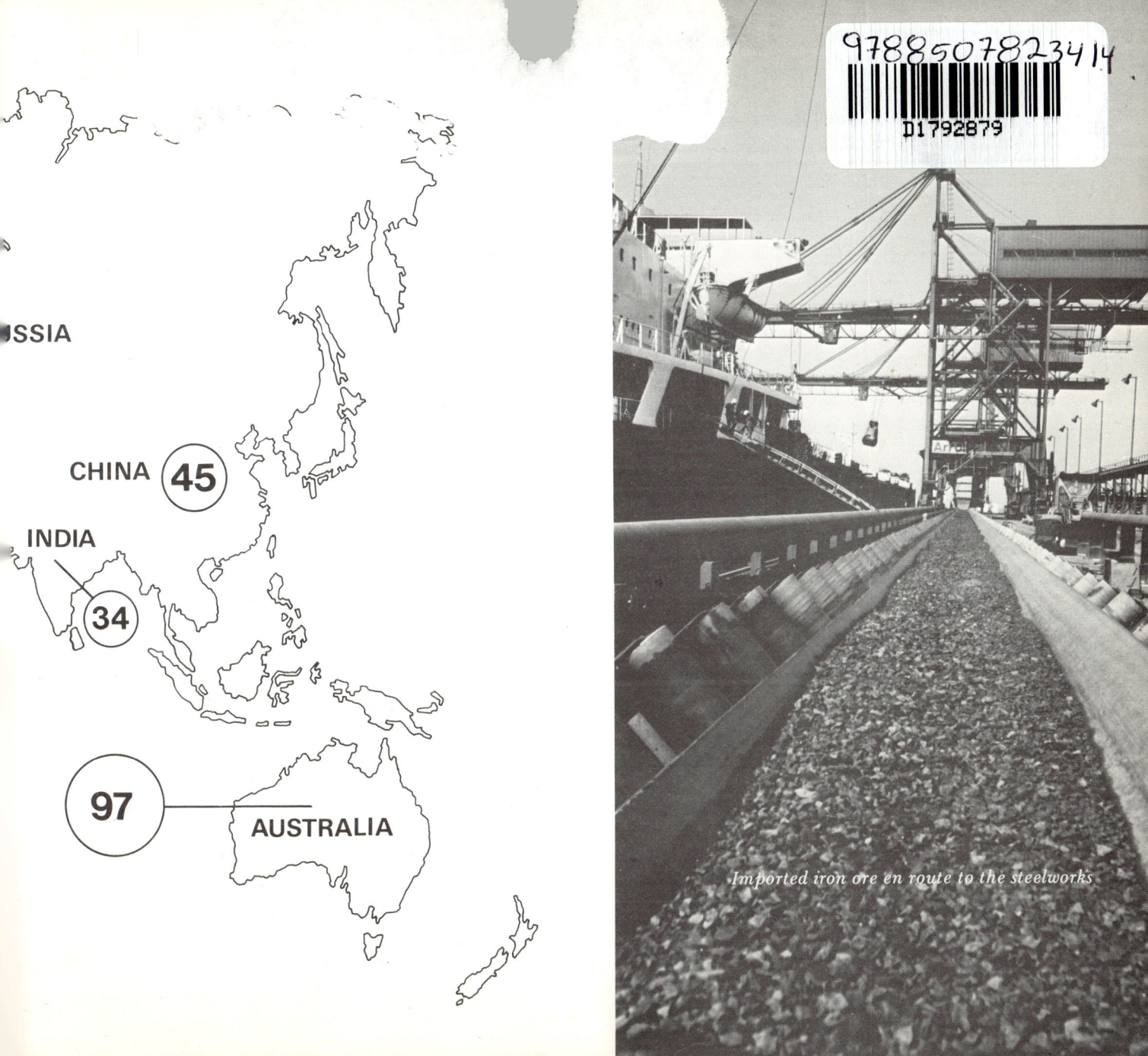

RUSSIA

CHINA 45

INDIA

34

97 AUSTRALIA

Imported iron ore en route to the steelworks

The author

PATRICK SAVILLE was born in Warwickshire near Birmingham, the metal trades centre in the English Midlands. He received an Honours Degree in Metallurgy at the University of Birmingham. After some industrial experience both at home and abroad, he entered the Government scientific service during the second World War.

In 1947 he became Information Officer at the Iron and Steel Institute, and when that became part of The Metals Society in 1974 he was made Manager, Information Services. He has written a number of articles and papers on the history of metallurgy and contributed the article on Sir Henry Bessemer to the new **Encyclopedia Britannica.**

Iron and steel

This book tells the story of iron and steel—the mines all over the world, the blast furnaces and the electric furnaces, the great rolling mills and forges which shape our steel. This is the story of how men use iron and steel in almost everything they do—at work, at play and at home.

Sampling steel from the furnace

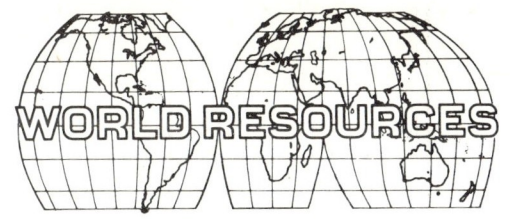

IRON
and
STEEL

J. P. Saville

Wayland

World Resources Series

Timber
Rubber
Iron and Steel
Sugar
Water
Seafood
Oil
Gas
Coal
Cocoa, Tea and Coffee
Grain
Meat
Nuclear Fuel
Gold and Silver
Soya
Alternative Energy

ISBN 85078 234 1
Copyright © 1976 Priory Press Limited
First published in 1976 by Priory Press Limited
49 Lansdowne Place, Hove, Sussex BN3 1HF
Second impression 1979
Third impression 1980
Printed and bound in Great Britain
at The Pitman Press, Bath

Contents

Iron and steel are all around you

Cast-iron, mild steel, alloy steels, stainless steels, sheet steel, steel wire . . . the kitchen abounds with iron and steel equipment and fittings: — cast-iron saucepans and cooker rings; mild steel sheet in the fridge, cooker and washing machine; alloy steels in the mixer, fridge and washing machine motors; stainless steel sink fittings and knives, and steel wire in the draining rack and the salad shaker. These are only some of the household uses of iron and steel

Iron and steel at home

Things made from iron and steel are in use everywhere. Did you have toast for breakfast? Most of the automatic toaster is steel—and you spread your butter and marmalade with steel knives. The milk you had with your cereal came from the fridge, and most of that is steel, too. On the cooker the grids and the burners are cast-iron and most of the rest is steel. So is the kettle, though if you have an electric kettle it will be aluminium, and so will many cheap kettles to put on the gas. But if you have an enamelled kettle, in blue or black or red or green, it is certainly made of steel underneath the enamel.

There were steel springs in your bed, more than likely, and if you had a bath when you got up, or before you went to bed, it might very well have been in a cast-iron bath. Many new baths are plastic, of course, or even fibre-glass, but there are plenty of cast-iron baths about. There was certainly steel in the alarm-clock that woke you up. If it was an electric clock, it would not work without steel in its motor, and if you wound it by hand, it was a steel spring that you wound up.

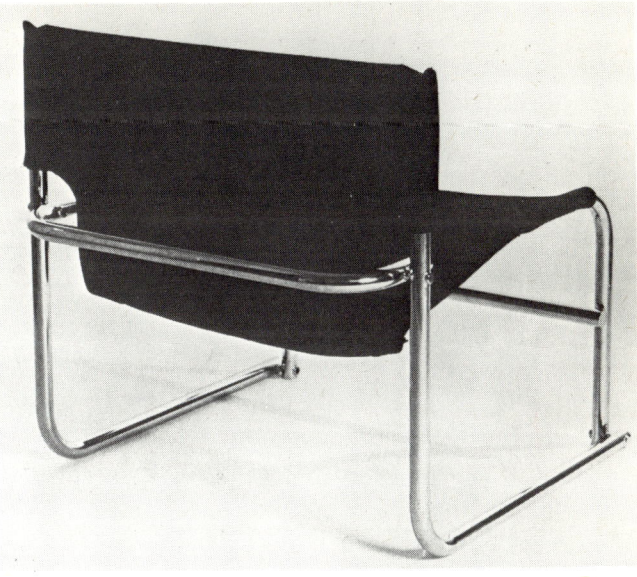

Below *Modern furniture makes effective and decorative use of tubular steel*

When you go off to school, do you ride down in the lift, or elevator? The cage you get into has steel framing and, to keep you safe, there are cast-iron shoes which slide on steel bars to guide it, while the steel rope lets you gently down. But perhaps you walk down to the street door? Then the stair may have steel handrails and if there is a staircarpet it is held down by steel tacks or steel clips. Iron and steel are everywhere.

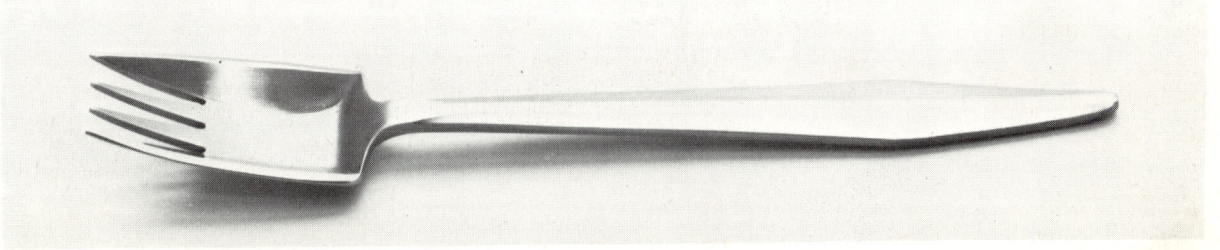

Above *The Splayd—a combined knife, fork and spoon! Though revolutionary in design it is made, traditionally, in stainless steel*

Iron and steel outside

Do you go to school on your bike? This is all steel, except for the tyres, the brakeblocks, and the seat of the saddle above its steel springs. But perhaps you go on the bus; the chassis and the bodywork are mostly steel, and so is a lot of the engine. Some of the most important parts of the engine are cast-iron. But you may go by subway, or the underground railway; here, the train runs on steel rails on its steel wheels, driven by electric motors mainly made of steel. If you have time to look at the sides of the tunnels, you will see that they are lined with thick cast-iron segments, held together with steel bolts. From the platform, you may ride up on an escalator; you can see for yourself the steel in the steps you stand on, though you cannot see the endless steel chains that carry the steps along. But perhaps you travel to school by car? This, like the bus, is mainly made of iron and steel; when you ride comfortably over a bumpy road, it is the steel suspension springs that make this possible. And for stopping, the car relies on good cast-iron brake drums.

If you are able to walk to school you will have time to notice many more uses of iron and steel. There are cast-iron lamp-posts, decorated with curlicues; the tall, elegant ones may be made of steel tubes, but if they are of concrete, as many are nowadays, they will be reinforced inside with steel bars. Look down at the pavement, and you will see manhole covers, for the gas, the electricity, the telephone, the water, the drains and the sewers, even, in some older neighbourhoods, for coal or coke. And far below the pavement there are many pipes and conduits, some made of iron, some of steel. Iron and steel are around us, above and below.

Though escalator steps may be of wood or aluminium alloy, the drive chains and structural trusses are always made from steel

Bikes—from granny's bone-shaker to modern racing machines—all rely heavily on steel. A variety of alloy steels make up the different steel components, ranging from tubular steel for the frame to steel wire for the spokes

Ironmaking

The past of ironmaking

Some metals are found in nature in their pure and solid state. Gold, for example, occurs in "nuggets", or is spread out in certain rocks in very fine particles of pure metal. Not so with iron; except for a few great meteorites from outer space, there are no solid lumps of iron to be found. Instead, iron only occurs as chemical compounds.

Most often the iron is combined with the gas oxygen, which is in the air we breathe, and the combination is called an oxide; ordinary rust is the commonest iron oxide. Or the compound may contain carbon as well as oxygen, and this will be called a carbonate. Some rocks are very largely made up of these compounds, and we then call them iron minerals, or iron ores. Any reddish-brown, softish rock probably contains a great deal of iron and could be an iron ore.

Although so much iron is locked up, as it were, in iron ores, early men found out, some three thousand years ago, that it was fairly simple to get the pure metal out again. All they needed to do

Above *Wood stacked for charcoal burning*

Above left *Limonite* (ferric oxide), *a common iron ore*

was to make a simple furnace of clay, like a big drainpipe standing on end, and put iron ore and charcoal into it. They set fire to the charcoal and blew the fire with simple bellows made of skins. As the charcoal burnt it gave off a poisonous gas, called carbon monoxide, and it is this gas which acted on the iron compounds in the ores and got the metal out.

Unfortunately, charcoal can be easily crushed, and won't bear much weight, and this means that the furnaces that early men built could not be very high, or hold much iron ore at a time. They could therefore only make a little iron at a time, enough for a few hoes or spearheads, spades, swords or arrowheads. Nevertheless, ancient civilizations, such as the Roman, were founded on iron made like this, even though they were never able to make enough iron for large constructions.

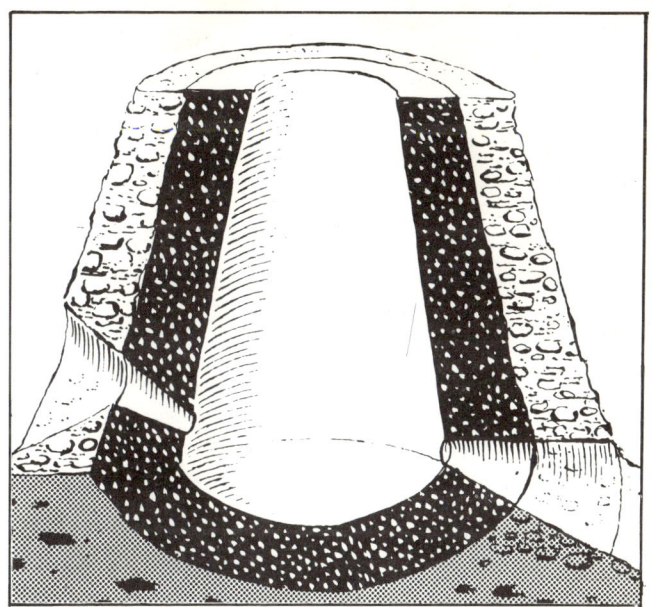

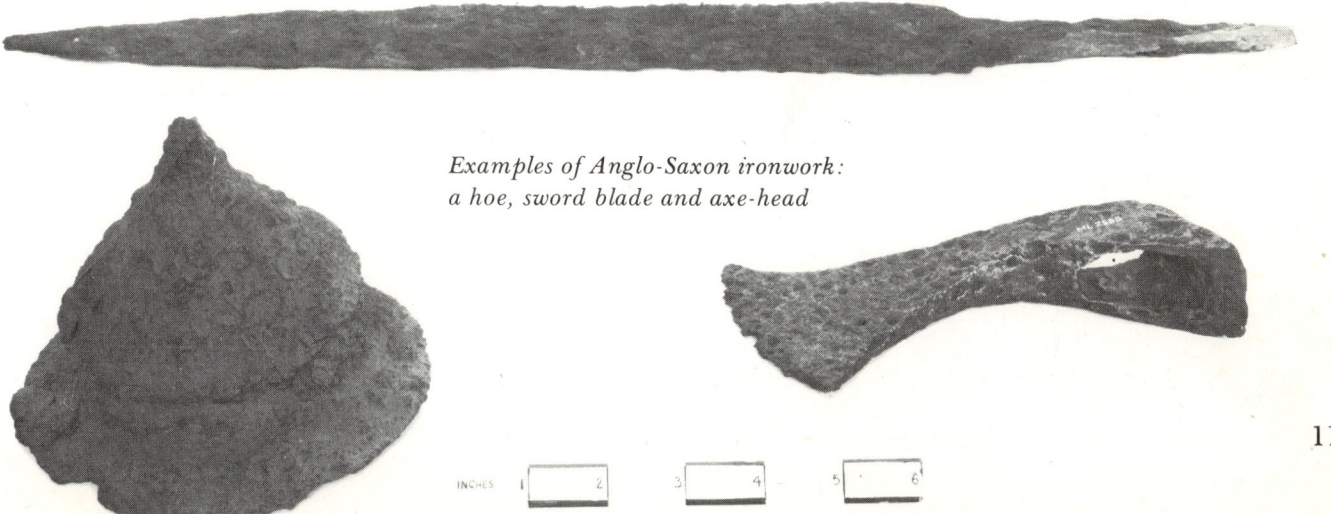

*Examples of Anglo-Saxon ironwork:
a hoe, sword blade and axe-head*

INCHES 1 2 3 4 5 6

11

Iron ore producers

We need so much iron ore today that there are many countries that do not have enough for their own use. Luckily, there are others that have a great deal more than they can use themselves, so that there is a world-wide trade in it. Great mountains of ore are mined out, crushed and sent all over the world. Ore from South America goes to the United States, and to Japan; ore from

Above *The Tazadit mine in Mauritania. This and other mines in that country produce an annual output of 9 million tons of rich iron ore*

Mining ore with a mechanical digger

Australia goes to Japan, too, and ore from North Africa and from Sweden is sent to England. There are Swedish mining companies in Liberia in West Africa which send the ore in many directions. Ores mined in one part of Russia travel a long way to other parts of that vast country. By sea, iron ore is carried in enormous ships nearly as big as oil tankers, and on land it travels in long trains of gigantic railway wagons. You may have seen them on their way to inland steelworks.

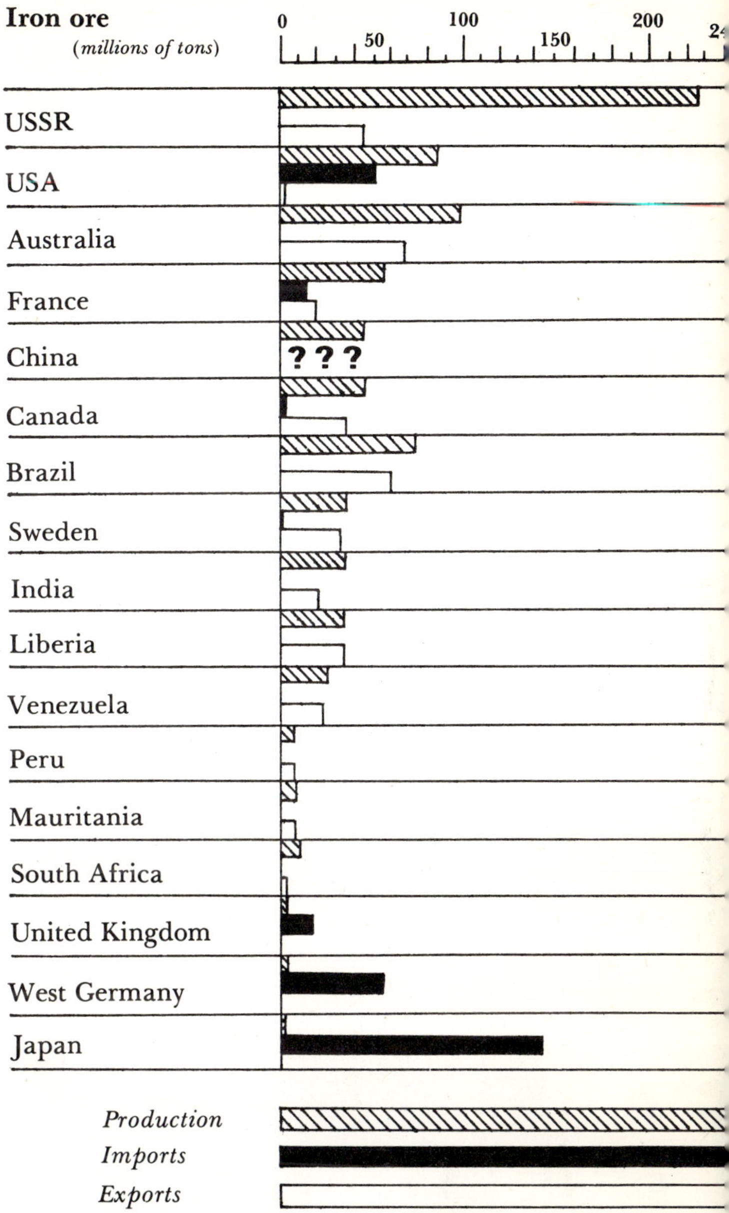

Iron ore
(millions of tons)

| Scale | 0 | 50 | 100 | 150 | 200 | 24 |

USSR

USA

Australia

France

China **? ? ?**

Canada

Brazil

Sweden

India

Liberia

Venezuela

Peru

Mauritania

South Africa

United Kingdom

West Germany

Japan

Production
Imports
Exports

Above *Iron ore: 1974 production, import and export figures for leading countries*

13

Below *Newly-made coke leaves the ovens*

The smelting process

To get the iron out of the ore, fuel is needed. The charcoal we spoke of earlier is no longer used, not only because it crushes so easily, but because the forests could not provide enough. But, just in time, it was found that coal could be used, if it was made into a kind of charcoal called coke. Coal could not be used just as it comes out of the ground, because it contains an element called sulphur which goes straight into iron, forms compounds with it, and makes it brittle. But if it is burned in covered heaps like wood, the sulphur is driven out, and what is left can be used like charcoal. It is hard, strong and full of little holes, which help it to burn easily. The first man to make coke in this way, specially for ironmaking, was Abraham Darby, of Coalbrookdale in Shropshire in England, more than 250 years ago; he could be called the father of ironmaking. Nowadays, the coal is burned in large "ovens" heated by gas, and useful products like gas, tar, ammonia and benzene are recovered.

Another thing which is needed in this ironmaking process, which we call smelting, is limestone. This is a fairly common rock which occurs in many forms, from chalk to marble, and its use in smelting is to combine with some of the other minerals in the iron ore and cause them to become liquid and flow away from the iron. The liquid that flows away is called "slag" and this has some uses of its own which will be described later on.

All these heavy and solid materials are needed to make iron. In addition, to speed up the process, we may need to blow oxygen into the furnaces, and use natural gas or oil to save solid fuel.

Below *Hot slag is transported to a slag pit*

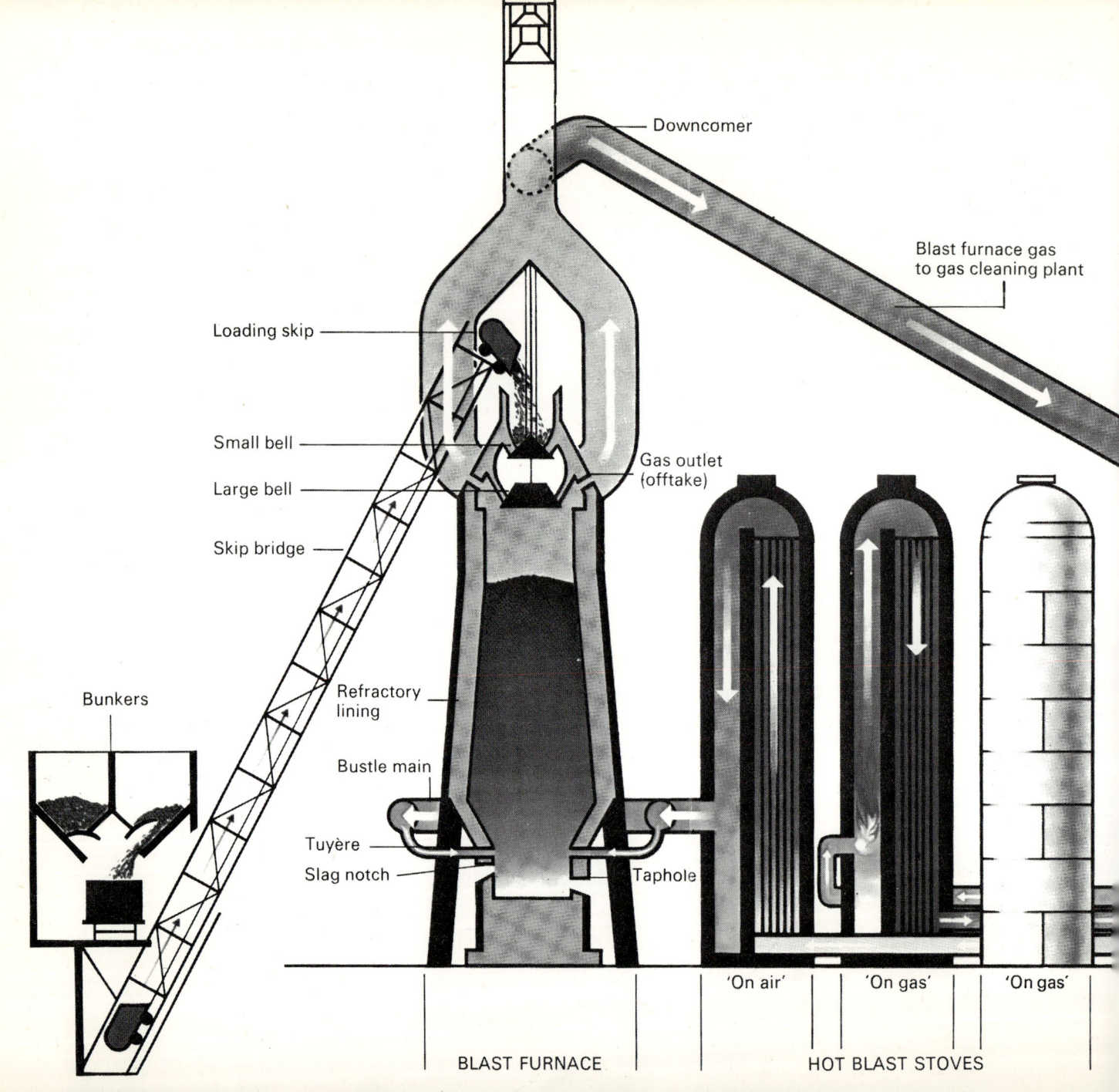

Downcomer

Blast furnace gas to gas cleaning plant

Loading skip

Small bell

Large bell

Gas outlet (offtake)

Skip bridge

Bunkers

Refractory lining

Bustle main

Tuyère

Slag notch

Taphole

'On air' 'On gas' 'On gas'

BLAST FURNACE HOT BLAST STOVES

Ironmaking furnaces

Today's furnaces are well over thirty metres high and are really tall cylinders of steel plate, lined with special bricks to stand the heat and the attack of molten metal and liquid slag. Even then, parts of the furnace will be cooled with water, because the heat is so intense. A number of men will be constantly looking after this cooling, making sure that there is enough water in every part, and that none of the plates is burning through.

As coke is more difficult to light and keep alight than charcoal, the furnace needs to have enormous quantities of air blown into it. This is why it is called a blast furnace; all this air is called "the blast". The air is heated before it is blown in, in heaters that are called "stoves" and stand nearly as high as the furnace; they work by burning the waste gas from the furnace. Many men will be looking after these, too, and more will be in charge of the blowers that push the air in. The air goes in just above the "hearth", through water-cooled nozzles called *tuyères*.

The hearth itself, the very bottom of the furnace where the iron collects, is like a brick-lined tank, perhaps forty feet wide and ten feet deep. The slag is run away at the top of this "tank" because it is lighter than the iron and floats on top of it, and the iron comes out at the bottom. More men will be at work down there, running the slag off, and opening the "taphole" for the iron, by breaking away the clay plug that was put in the last time the furnace was tapped.

Blast Furnace gas having passed through dust catchers and spray chambers goes through electrostatic precipitators or other gas cleaning plant to a gasholder.

Clean gas is brought back and burnt in the stoves to heat them.

Waste gas passes to stack

Cold air flow enters pre-heated stove on line and is heated as it passes through on its way to the tuyères in the Blast Furnace.

DUST CATCHER

WET SCRUBBER

17

18   **Above** *Burning out the taphole prior to tapping the iron from a blast furnace*

Above *Charging molten iron into a steelmaking furnace*

Casting molten iron into pigs

Iron leaves the furnace

You can see that although there are great similarities between the little furnaces of primitive man, and the gigantic blast furnaces of today, there must be some differences. Indeed there are, the greatest being that his furnaces produced a few pounds of pasty iron at a time, and ours can run for years and produce millions of tons of liquid metal. What is more, he could take his lump, or "bloom" as it was often called, and hammer it at once into something useful. Our metal, being liquid, has no shape of its own, and

we have to pour it into something or other to set. As it comes out of the furnace, therefore, we either let it run into depressions in a bed of sand in front of the furnace, or into moulds, to give us something to handle.

A lot of iron, as we shall see, is not treated in that way at all; great ladles, mounted on rails, are brought up and it runs into them to keep molten till we can turn it into steel. But for the present, we will follow the progress of the solid iron; this is called "pig-iron" at this stage, because the shape of the depressions made in the sand bed look rather like rows of piglets feeding from a sow.

Cast-iron and its uses

The material from the blast furnace is, as we said, called pig-iron. In its passage down the furnace over the red-hot coke, when it was exposed to all the gases, it has picked up a lot of the element carbon—well over three per cent, in fact—and this is what makes it so liquid. But as it goes solid, some of the carbon stays in the iron, making it hard, but a lot more comes out in large soft flakes making the metal brittle and easy to break. In fact, the iron may run like water, but it sets like ice. This means that we can't hammer it into shape, of course. But because it runs so well, we can pour it into moulds like jelly. And, although it is so brittle and won't stand shocks or bending, it is hard enough and strong enough to bear heavy loads.

The moulds we use are not quite like jelly moulds; some are made of metal, but most are made from heat-resisting sand shaped round a wooden model—called a "pattern"—of the thing we want to make. If we want hollow objects, we put a "core"—another specially shaped block of this sand—into the mould, and the metal fills the space between them. You can see that a bell, or a cooking pot, could be easily made by such a process, but it can also be applied to really complicated things. Car cylinder blocks, for example, are made by this process.

There are many hollow objects in common use that could only be made by such a method, like traffic bollards, and big gas and water pipes. But there are a lot more solid things, and flat things too, that are made by casting, and these are everywhere; manhole covers in the street, grids on gas and electric stoves, the brake-blocks for trains and the "chairs" that hold the rails onto the sleepers.

Some of the most important things made by casting are the frames of machine-tools. These are the machines that make other machines by drilling and turning and milling, removing surplus metal to make shapes that cannot be cast or made in other ways. For making these machines, cast-iron is essential.

Above *Heavy cast-iron tanks and piping at a gasworks*

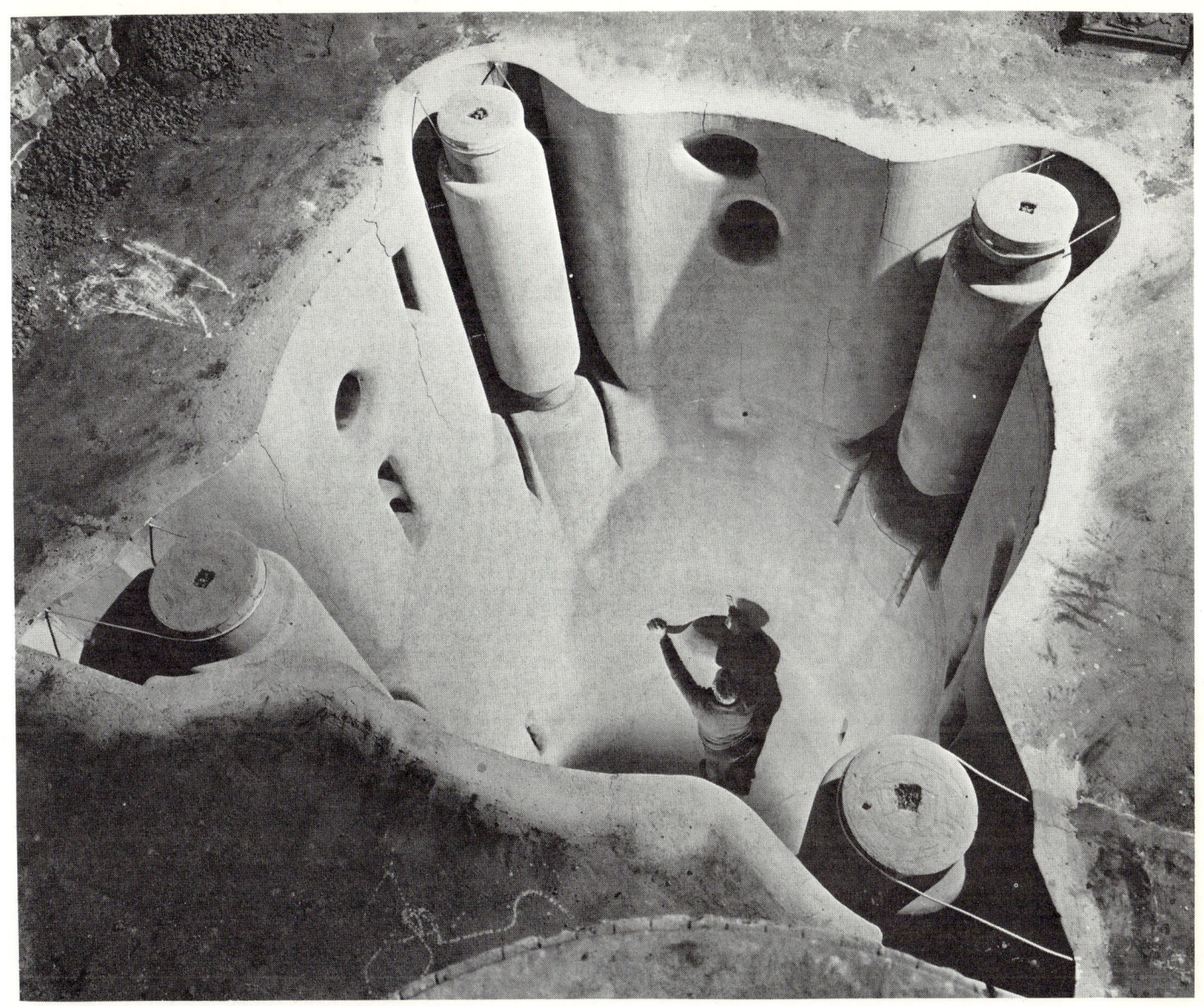

Above *Finishing the sand mould for a huge (4,000 ton) extrusion press cylinder*

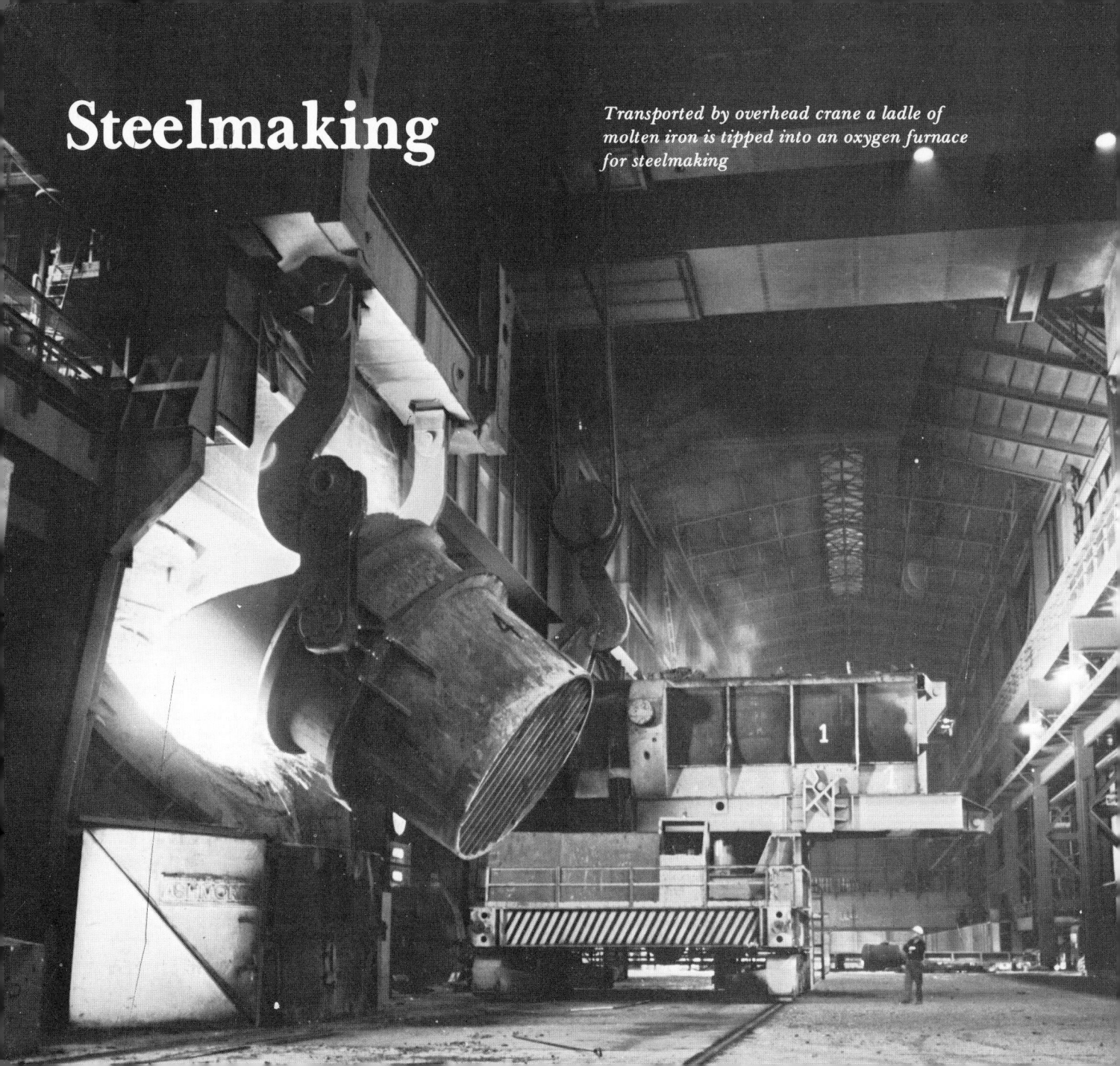

Steelmaking

Transported by overhead crane a ladle of
molten iron is tipped into an oxygen furnace
for steelmaking

Turning iron into steel

There are many things for which cast-iron would be hard enough, and strong enough, if only it were prepared to bend a little and recover again, as a tree does in the wind. But instead it snaps straight off. If we heat cast-iron objects up again in sand, or in powdered iron ore, we can give them a little of this power to resist shock or bending, but the process takes a long time, and the effects don't go far into the metal, so that it is only suitable for small things.

It is far better to turn the original pig-iron into steel. Indeed, if we want metal for beams, and for bridge girders, for plates for ships and tanks, for wires, for rails for the railway—for any thing that must give a little under a load—we simply have to do so.

Above *Large steel spans will carry a new road between Rio de Janeiro and Niteroi in Brazil*

It is a fairly easy process; as the blast furnace has added carbon to the iron, so the steelmaking processes take it out again. Not quite all of it though, and sometimes we have to put a little back, and at the same time add other metals to give the steel special qualities. If we have the metal hot from the blast furnace, we can save both heat and time. You will remember that we spoke of the iron being poured into ladles mounted on rails; of course these ladles are not at all like soup-ladles, they have simply kept the name from when they were small enough to be handled by one or two men. Now they are like enormous cauldrons and hold fifty to a hundred tons; they may have wheels and run on rails, or they may be transported by overhead travelling cranes to the furnaces where the iron is made into steel.

23

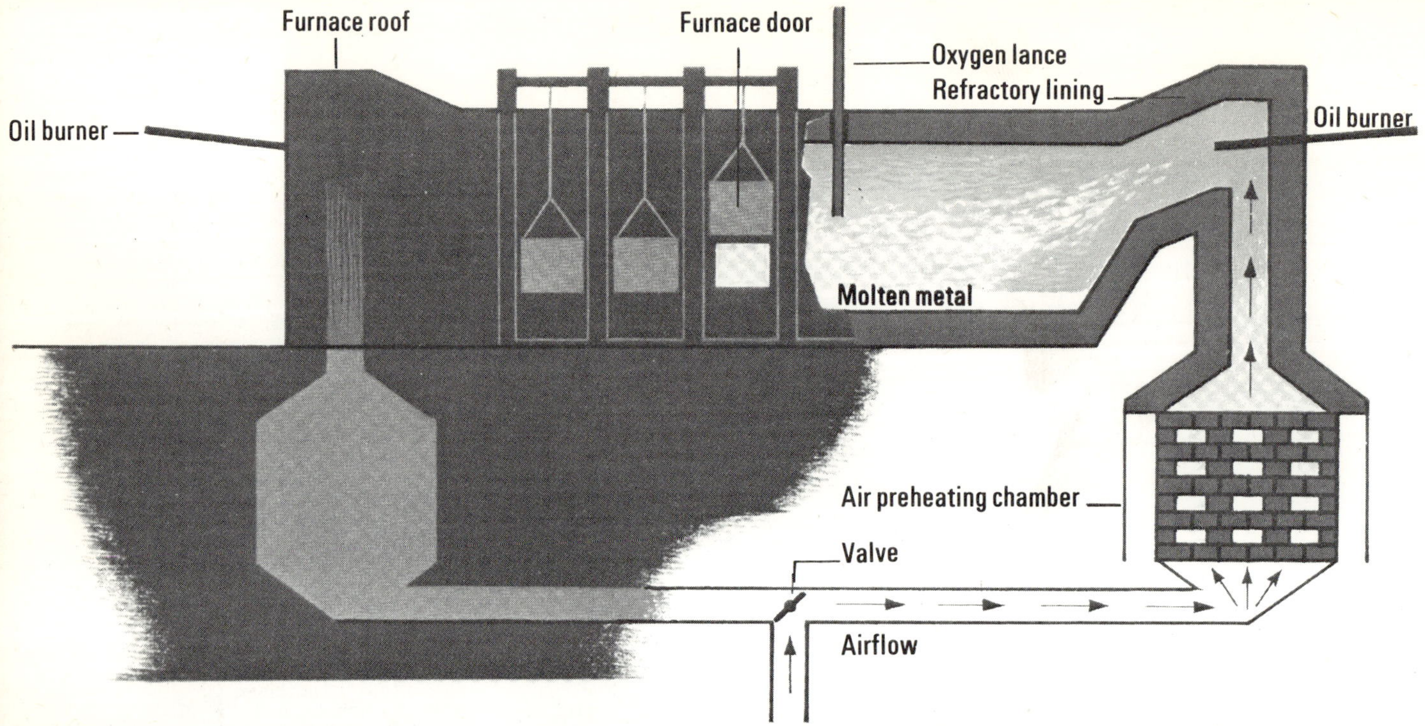

Furnace roof

Furnace door

Oil burner

Oxygen lance

Refractory lining

Oil burner

Molten metal

Air preheating chamber

Valve

Airflow

24

CHARGING SCRAP

CHARGING HOT METAL

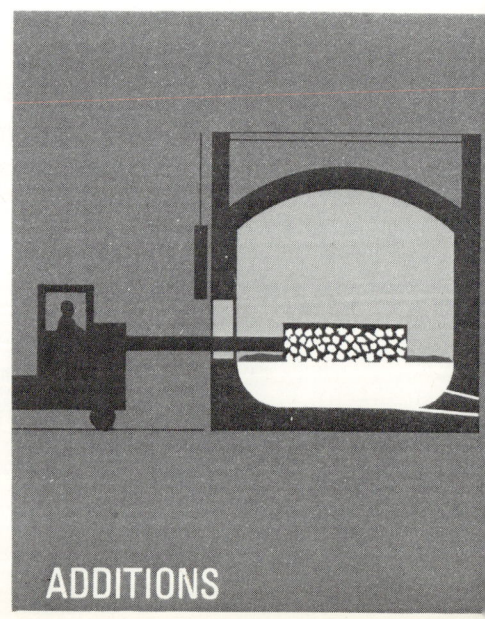

ADDITIONS

The open-hearth furnace

Up until fairly recently, the "open-hearth furnace" was almost the only type used. This was like a long shallow bath with a roof, all made of, or lined with, heat-resisting bricks or other heat-resisting material. From the ends, gas or oil flames beat down, and the shape of the roof forced the flames down onto the molten metal. To work the process, iron ore was thrown in to provide the oxygen to burn out the carbon. It was a slow process; even if this bath held two hundred or more tons, it might still take ten hours to turn it all into steel. Sometimes jets of oxygen were blown down from the roof to speed things up, and this had quite an effect. But now something very much faster has replaced this method.

Below *The furnace in action (front view)*

SAMPLING

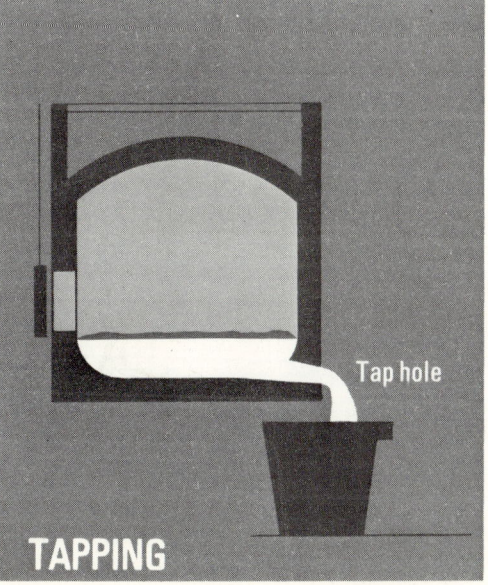

TAPPING

Tap hole

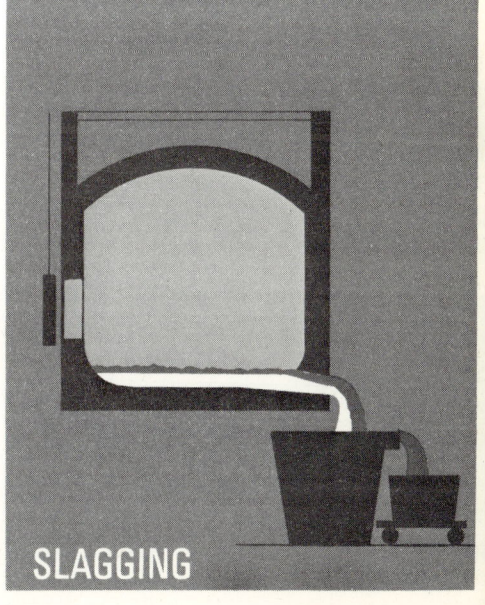

SLAGGING

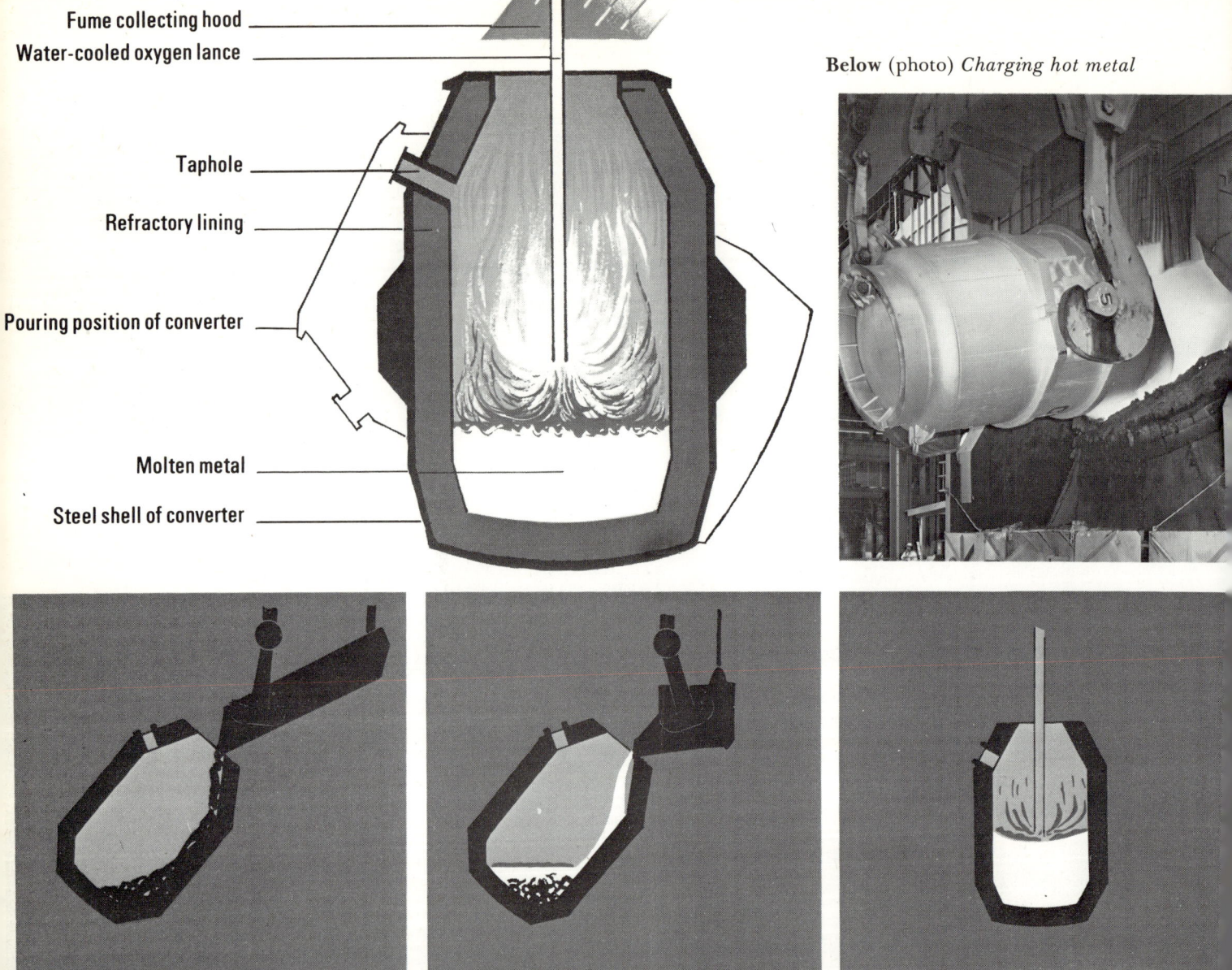

Fume collecting hood

Water-cooled oxygen lance

Below (photo) *Charging hot metal*

Taphole

Refractory lining

Pouring position of converter

Molten metal

Steel shell of converter

26

CHARGING SCRAP

CHARGING HOT METAL

'BLOW'

The oxygen furnace

Nowadays most steel is made by a process called oxygen steelmaking. This takes place in what is, in principle, a very simple furnace indeed, no more than a very large steel vessel, rather like a jam-jar in shape but closing in a little at the top. This furnace is lined with heat-resisting bricks. (Without heat-resisting materials, known as "refractories", there would be no steelmaking by any process.) The molten iron is poured into this jam-jar, and through a jet poked into the narrowed top, oxygen, or air with a lot of oxygen added, is blown straight down onto the metal. It burns the carbon out very quickly, and two hundred to four hundred tons of iron can be "converted" into steel in twenty minutes.

In the course of this burning, a great deal of heat is produced, and a lot of cold scrap iron can be put in to cool and be recycled. But still it is very hot, so that the jet, which is called a lance, has to be cooled with water to prevent it melting away. It has a water jacket around it, with constantly flowing water. A great deal of hot gas comes off, so hot that it can be used to raise steam, and so rich in carbon monoxide that it can be burnt to get still more heat out of it. This gas is caught in a hood over the converter, and you can see that what with this, and the gear needed to raise and lower the lance, the whole thing is not quite so simple as it might seem. But the whole process has been developed in a very short period of time — less than twenty years — and most of the world's steel is now made in this way.

SAMPLING

TAPPING

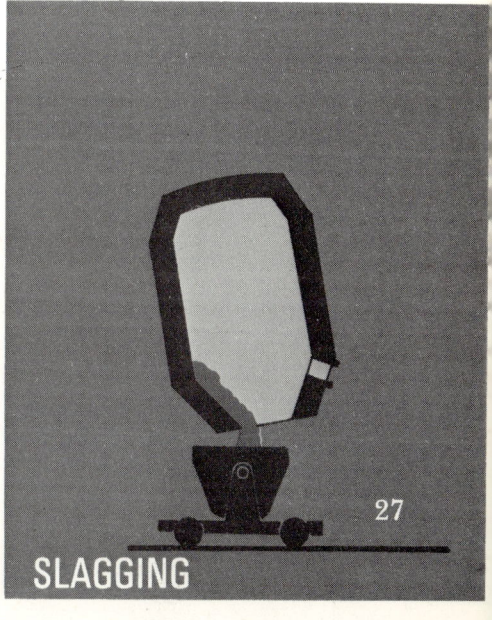

SLAGGING

27

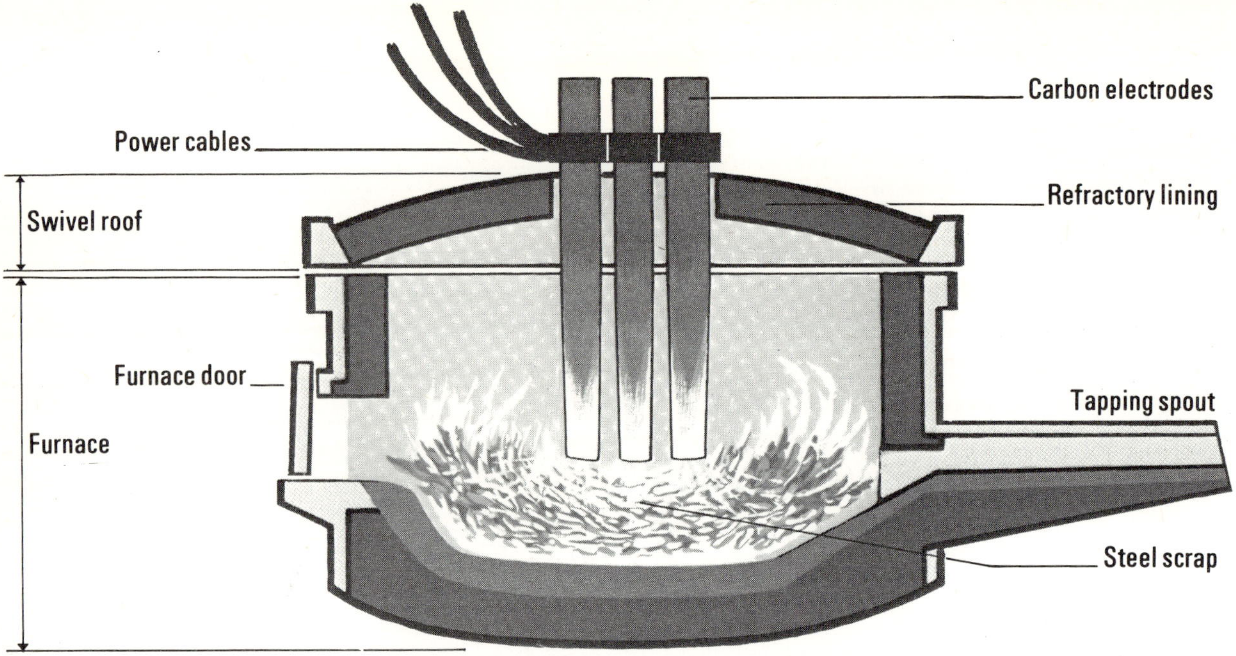

Carbon electrodes

Power cables

Swivel roof

Refractory lining

Furnace door

Tapping spout

Furnace

Steel scrap

28
CHARGING SCRAP

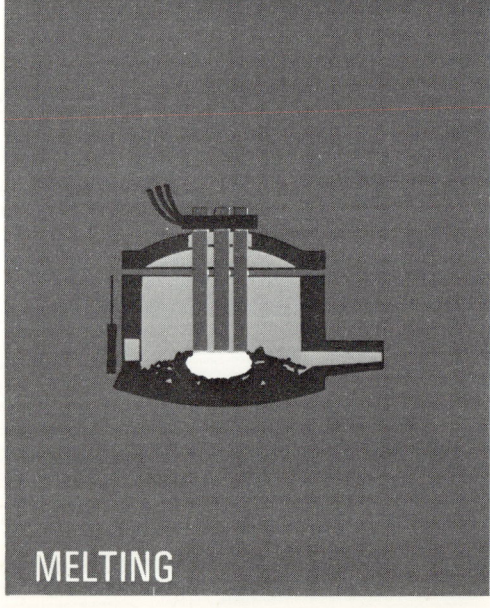

MELTING

ADDITIONS

The electric furnace

Of course, as everywhere else, there are some things you can do better by electricity, and electric steelmaking is the only method for some types of steel. If you pass a powerful electric current between thick carbon rods—as used to be done in searchlights and cinema projectors—you get a great deal of heat as well as light. In the electric arc furnace, the current flows between very thick carbon rods and the metal to be melted, melting the metal very quickly indeed. It is all pure melting; there is no chemical reaction. And because of the burning carbon of the electrodes, there is no loss of metal. You will remember that burning carbon produces metal from oxides, and not the other way round. So we can melt up scrap containing other metals than iron, and add other metals too, to make special steels, like tool steels or stainless steel. Making these mixed metals is called "alloying" and the results are called alloy steel.

Charging scrap

SAMPLING

SLAGGING

TAPPING

The shaping of steel

Cast steel and ingots

As we can pour iron into moulds, to make things, so we can cast steel. Steel, even when it is poured into moulds, is stronger than iron and has some flexibility, so that steel castings are used for a lot of things, such as the big teeth on grabs and bulldozers, the pivots you see under some bridges and the big frames of a lot of ships' engines.

But most steel is not used in the cast form. Shipbuilders need great thick sheets of steel which they call plates, car manufacturers need thinner metal that they can form into bodies and wings, and the makers of food cans and oil drums and other containers want their steel very thin and in great length. This is called strip. All these forms of steel come, in the first place, from "ingots".

In the furnaces we have mentioned—the open hearth, the oxygen furnace and the electric furnace—two hundred to three hundred tons of steel are ready at once. This is poured out into big ladles—very like those in which the iron from the blast furnace comes to the steel furnace—and carried to the "ingot moulds". These are made of cast-iron, very thick, round or square, and about five times as high as they are wide. They will hold fifteen or twenty tons of steel when they are filled from the ladle. The steel soon sets solid in them, but it is not allowed to go cold. As soon as it has set enough to be handled, a crane-man will pull the ingot out of the mould with his overhead crane, and put it into a furnace to reach an even heat throughout. Then the ingot goes to the rolling mill.

Above *Teeming hot metal into ingot moulds*

INGOT CASTING

Ingots are a convenient form in which to handle steel, and the molten steel is released through the base of a ladle into moulds. When the metal has solidified, the mould is removed. Each ingot is of carefully pre-arranged dimensions and weight from which articles of required size can be rolled or forged. In the rolling process, red hot ingots are passed between heavy rolls and shaped into slabs, blooms or heavy sections. In forging, the ingots are pressed or hammered into shape.

SPECIAL CASTING

Steel castings vary in size from small precision parts for general engineering purposes to Forging Press Cylinders, Turbine Casings or Stern Frames for large ships. The molten steel is teemed [poured] into sand moulds which are broken up when the steel has solidified to remove the castings.

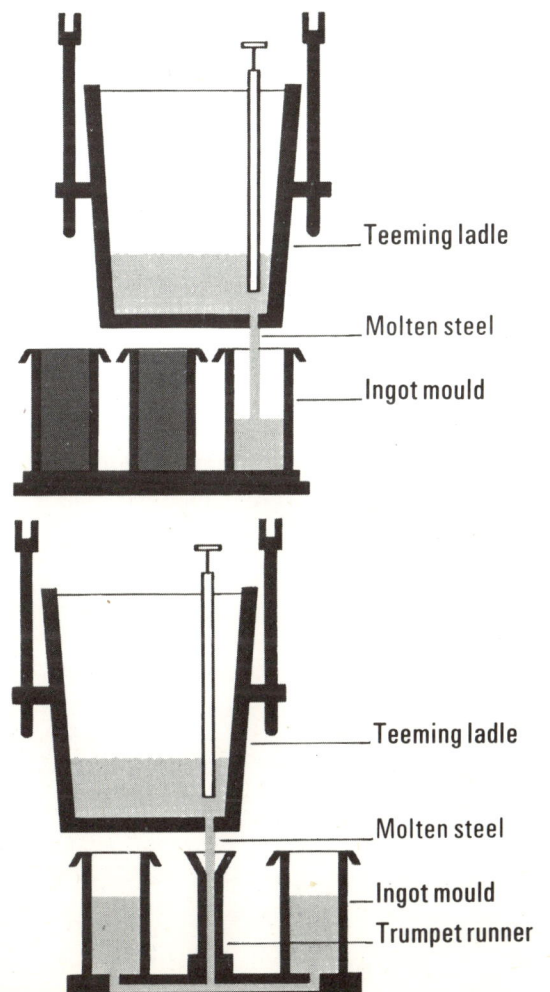

Teeming ladle

Molten steel

Ingot mould

Teeming ladle

Molten steel

Ingot mould

Trumpet runner

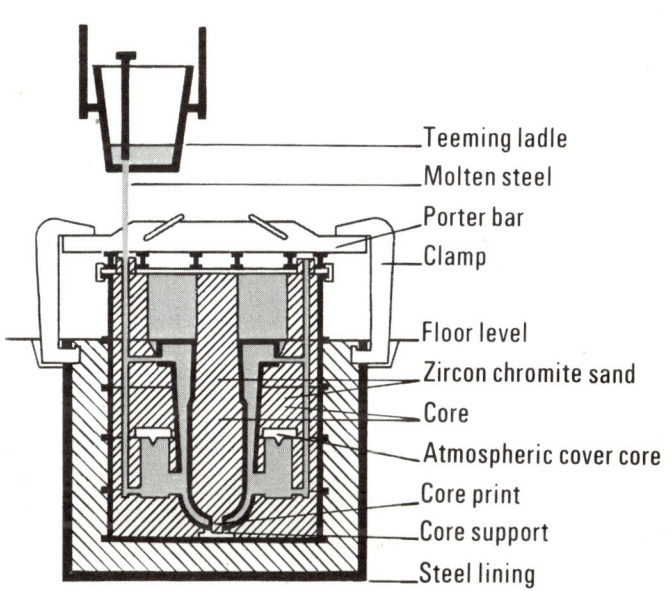

Teeming ladle

Molten steel

Porter bar

Clamp

Floor level

Zircon chromite sand

Core

Atmospheric cover core

Core print

Core support

Steel lining

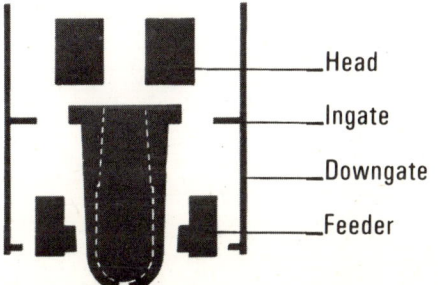

Head

Ingate

Downgate

Feeder

31

The rolling mill

The rolling mill is like an enormous metal mangle, or wringer, driven by powerful motors. The rolls can be brought closer together, or separated to produce different thicknesses of plate and strip steel. Shipbuilders want flat plates, so the rolls must be smooth, like rolling pins for pastry; as are the rolls that thin the steel still further for carbody material, and thin strip for food cans and so on. The ingots they start from won't be really square, they will be more brick-shaped—they are often called "slabs". But if we want to roll beams for buildings, with cross sections like H or L, or the enormous quantities of round and square rods used for engineering purposes, we don't use smooth rolls at all. The rolls used to make these have grooves and ridges fitting into one another, and all kinds of shapes can be made.

Great skill is needed by the men who operate these machines, who are simply called "rollers".

Strip rolling: *The scale breaker removes an oxide skin (scale) formed during reheating . . .*

. . . the clean slab is rolled thinner by the rolls of the roughing section . . .

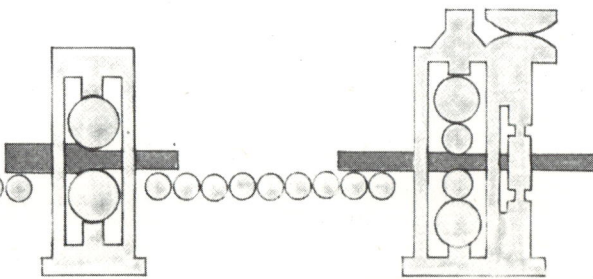

32

Slab Re-heating Furnace   **Scale Breaker**   **Roughing Stand**

They must control the speed, and the distances apart of the rolls, so that exactly the shape needed is produced. All the steel in ships, in buildings, and in all the millions of miles of rails throughout the world owes its shape to the rollers' care in controlling their powerful machines.

. . . is rolled to its final thickness . . .

. . . then cooled by water and coiled

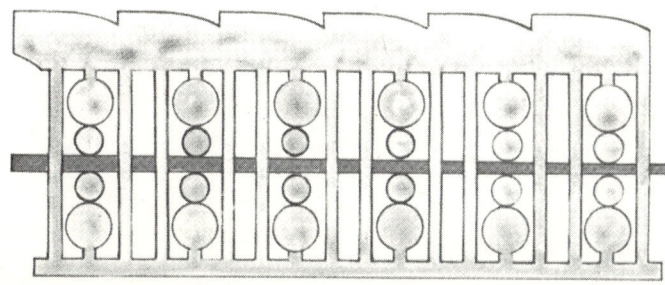

Finishing Stands

Quenching

Coiler

Eight steel blooms passing from the
cooling chamber to the straightening rolls
in the continuous casting process

34

Continuous casting

Nowadays, although there are plenty of ingots still being cast and rolled, a process called "continuous casting" is coming in. Instead of being poured into a lot of ingot moulds, the steel is poured into one only! But this is a rather special mould; it is made of copper so that the steel will not stick to it, and it is water-cooled. Moreover, the bottom is movable. Steel is poured in, and as soon as it sets at the bottom, the movable part is pulled out with the steel firmly attached to it, and more metal is added at the top. This cools and joins to the bottom part. By continuously adding metal at the top, and moving the solidified metal on, "ingots" hundreds of yards long can be made. Of course, they are cut up into lengths, and rolled.

The advantages of this process are that there is very little waste—no part of the cut lengths is scrap, as is the case with ingots—fewer ingot moulds are needed, and the ingots can be narrower across. This means that less powerful rolling mills can be used, and less fuel is needed for reheating the ingots because they come continuously to the rolling mill. The process is used on a lot of common steels designed for construction work.

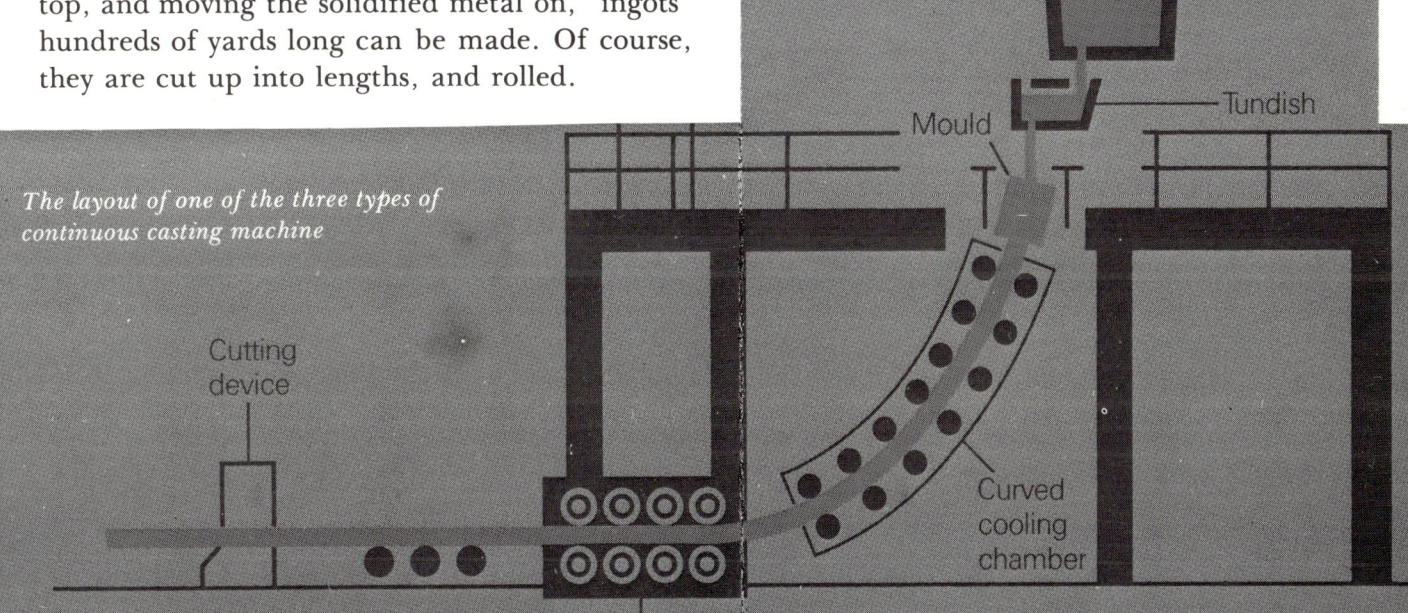

The layout of one of the three types of continuous casting machine

Cutting device

Withdrawal and straightening rolls

Mould

Ladle

Tundish

Curved cooling chamber

Curved mould

35

Steel pipemaking

You might not think that gas pipes or water pipes were made in a rolling mill; but there are many mills doing just this. They start with a round ingot with a hole pierced down the middle; the rolls have semicircular grooves opposite each other, and the ingot is put over a strong steel bar, called a mandrel. As the metal stretches out in its passage through the mill, the bar keeps the central hole truly round. In this manner, the miles of tubes and pipes that carry water and natural gas and oil all over the country are made. Smaller pipes, like electric-wiring conduit, are often made by bending strip into a circle or spiral, and welding the edges together—but, of course, the strip had to be made in a rolling mill first!

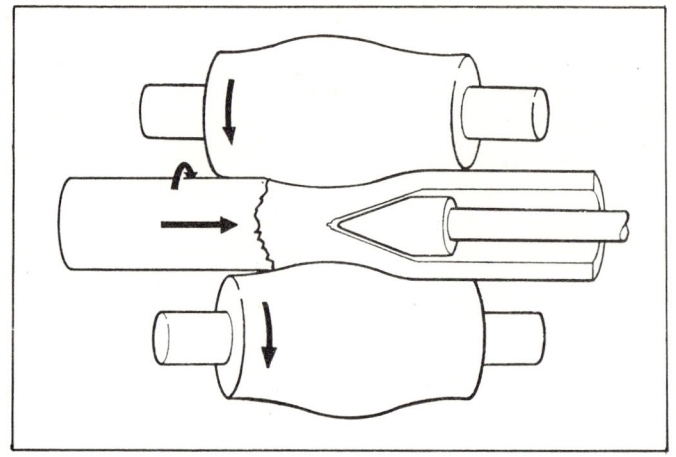

Above *The barrel-shaped rolls and mandrel of a tube piercing mill*

Below *Pipemaking from strip steel: welding the spiral together*

Above *Steel bars for use in reinforced concrete and building work*

Below *Coil upon coil of wire ranged between the wire-drawing machines*

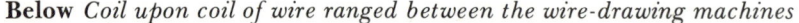

Making steel wire

People use a great deal of wire, in one way or another. Paper clips are made of wire, and so are pins and needles. There is wire in the armouring of power cables, as you may have seen if they have laid them in your street, and there is wire in the casings of tyres. There is wire in chip-frying baskets and vegetable racks at home, and wire in the lift-cables in every block of flats. There is wire to make the guy-ropes of television masts, and wire in reinforced concrete.

All this wire went through the rolling mill before it became anything like as thin. It was rolled down from the big ingot—in stages of course—into a rod about half an inch across, and so long that it had to be coiled up on a reel. Now it could be drawn down into wire. Drawn is the right word because it is then pulled through a succession of smaller and smaller holes called "dies", to the thickness needed, which might be no more than that of a hair. Powerful machines are needed for this, and big drums to wind the wire upon as it comes from the dies, and special furnaces to anneal (soften) it, from time to time, as it gets hard from being worked down.

Left *Fine wire drawing. The wire is drawn down through progressively smaller-holed dies (one is being threaded in the picture) to the required thickness*

39

Forging

But we can't roll everything. You can roll pastry as thin as you like, but you don't make a loaf of bread with a rolling pin. To make a lot of things in steel, we have to go back to the way of the blacksmith with his hammer, beating the hot steel into the shape he wants it. We call this forging,

and the place where it is done, the forge. The hammer is not swung by a man, though; it is lifted by steam or compressed air above the anvil and guided by a strong frame to fall exactly in the right place. The smith is still in control of this—nowadays he is called a forge-man—and he could drop his hammer lightly enough just to crack an eggshell. But he is more likely to be forging an ingot into the driving shaft for a steam or motor ship, or the rotor of a steam turbine for a power-station.

He won't be doing all this by himself. The steel will be held, and twisted and turned, by other big machines called manipulators, with skilled men to operate them. That sort of forging is rather like using modelling clay, where you can make a square lump round, or make a piece longer or shorter by pressing it out between your hands. But if we fit special tools to the hammer and the anvil so that there is a hollow space between them when they come together, we can make complicated things, like crankshafts for engines, connecting-rods for them, spanners, wrenches, knife-blades, scissors and many other things, large and small.

But, with all these big machines, the blacksmith is not out of business yet. He may use a small power hammer and not his own strength, but his skill in knowing just where to strike is still needed for the treatment of certain special steels, or to make special forgings where only a few items are needed.

40   **Above** *A large crankshaft for a ship's engine is set up for hardening*

Right *The first stage: a hot ingot is reshaped in the forging press*

41

What else can be done to steel?

Annealing and hardening

Sometimes, when steel has been worked into the right shape by the methods we have been describing, it is not quite ready for its final use. The processes may have made it a bit stiff and tired, as it were, particularly if they were carried out when it was beginning to get cool. In this state it will not stretch much before it breaks, however strong it may be. When steel is under a load, as it is in engines or bridges, for example, it needs to be able to stretch a bit and relax again, like elastic. If it loses this ability, we can give it back by heating

Below *An annealing furnace* (top of picture) *is lowered onto a steel cylinder which is to be treated*

Below right *Several examples of cutting tools made from high-speed steels*

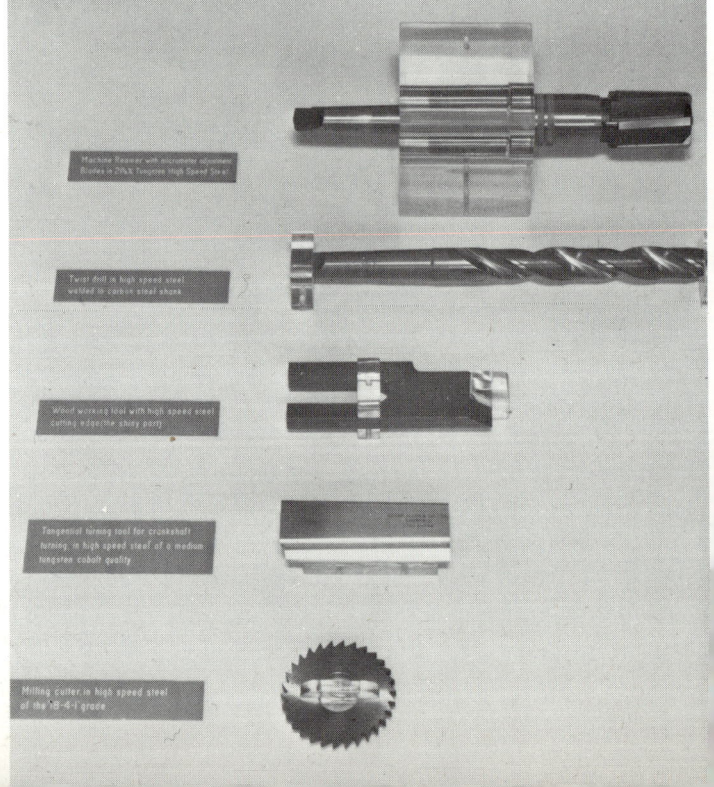

it again to a proper temperature, a process that is called annealing. Sometimes, however, the steel is needed for cutting things, and for this it has to be very hard. So, when cutting tools are made, they are finally heated to more than a red hot temperature, and "quenched" by putting them rapidly into water or oil. This makes them very hard indeed, but rather brittle. The brittleness is removed by "tempering". That is, heating them gently again to a lower temperature, which takes away the brittleness and leaves most of the hardness.

The heat treatment department in a major steelworks

you can see many factory chimneys made of steel coated with aluminium in this way. The coating resists fumes and smoke very well.

The tin can, which so much food comes in nowadays, is not made of tin, but only coated with it. Tin is a metal which resists food and fruit juices very well. This *tinned* steel used to be made by dipping the steel sheets into molten tin, but it is not made that way any more. Tin is a very expensive metal and in the hot-dipping process very much more tin sticks on than is really needed. So the coating is done nowadays by electroplating.

Protecting steel

A lot of steel is ready for use as it is, except that we may want to use it in places where the weather or other things will get at it and cause it to rust. So steel sheet for roofing is coated with zinc by dipping it into a molten bath of that metal. We call this galvanized iron. (Galvanized is an old word meaning electroplated, which happens to have stuck to zinc-coated steel, though it is wrong, as you will see when we describe electroplating.) Zinc is not the only metal which can be put onto steel by "hot-dipping". Aluminium can, too, and

44

That is, by passing an electric current from a lump of the metal tin, through a solution of chemical compounds of that metal in a big tank, to the steel. Tin comes out of the liquid onto the steel, and tin goes from the lump into the liquid to replace it. This is a slow process, so that we can make our layer as thick or thin as we like. As really very little is needed to protect the steel, it is a process very economical in its use of a costly metal.

Metals are not always protected by other metals, of course. There is plenty of paint about, as you can see. Ships' bottoms will be coated with

Below *Plastic-coated steel furniture*

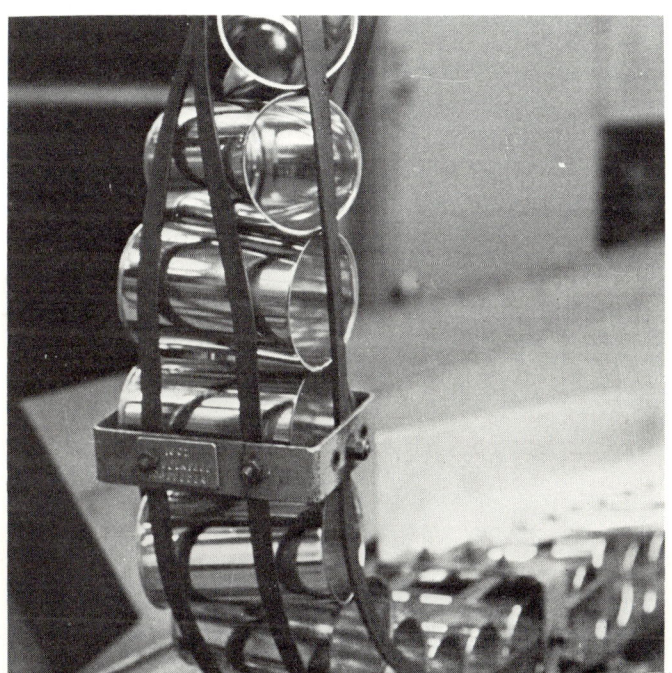

Above *Tin cans on a baked bean production line*

kinds of paint which not only resist the growth of weeds and barnacles, but will actually poison them. Car bodies do not need the poison, but they do need the paint. The underparts of a car may be given special kinds of paint to resist the salt and grit that is spread on the roads in winter. Steel can be given a good strong colourful coating with plastics. A lot of office furniture, like filing cabinets and cupboards, is being made of steel covered in this way. And we must not forget one of the oldest coatings of all, enamel. This is really a kind of glass, and can be coloured like glass, as all our enamelled saucepans and casseroles show us.

45

How many kinds of steel are there?

There are very many kinds indeed, because a steel can be found for almost any use you can think of. The commonest kind is called mild steel, and many of the largest man-made objects you are likely to see are made of it. Its virtues are that it is strong enough for most purposes and that it does not need further treatment by heat. This is the steel for bridges, tall buildings, pylons, pipelines, boiler plates, ship plates, and of course it is used for sheets and strip. But for engineering purposes, such as gears and other parts of engines, mild steel is not hard enough, and would soon wear out by rubbing away. To harden it we can leave a little carbon in it in the making, or add a little while it is still molten. And a steel of this sort can be made harder by the same method of "quenching" and "tempering" that we use for cutting tools, as was described earlier.

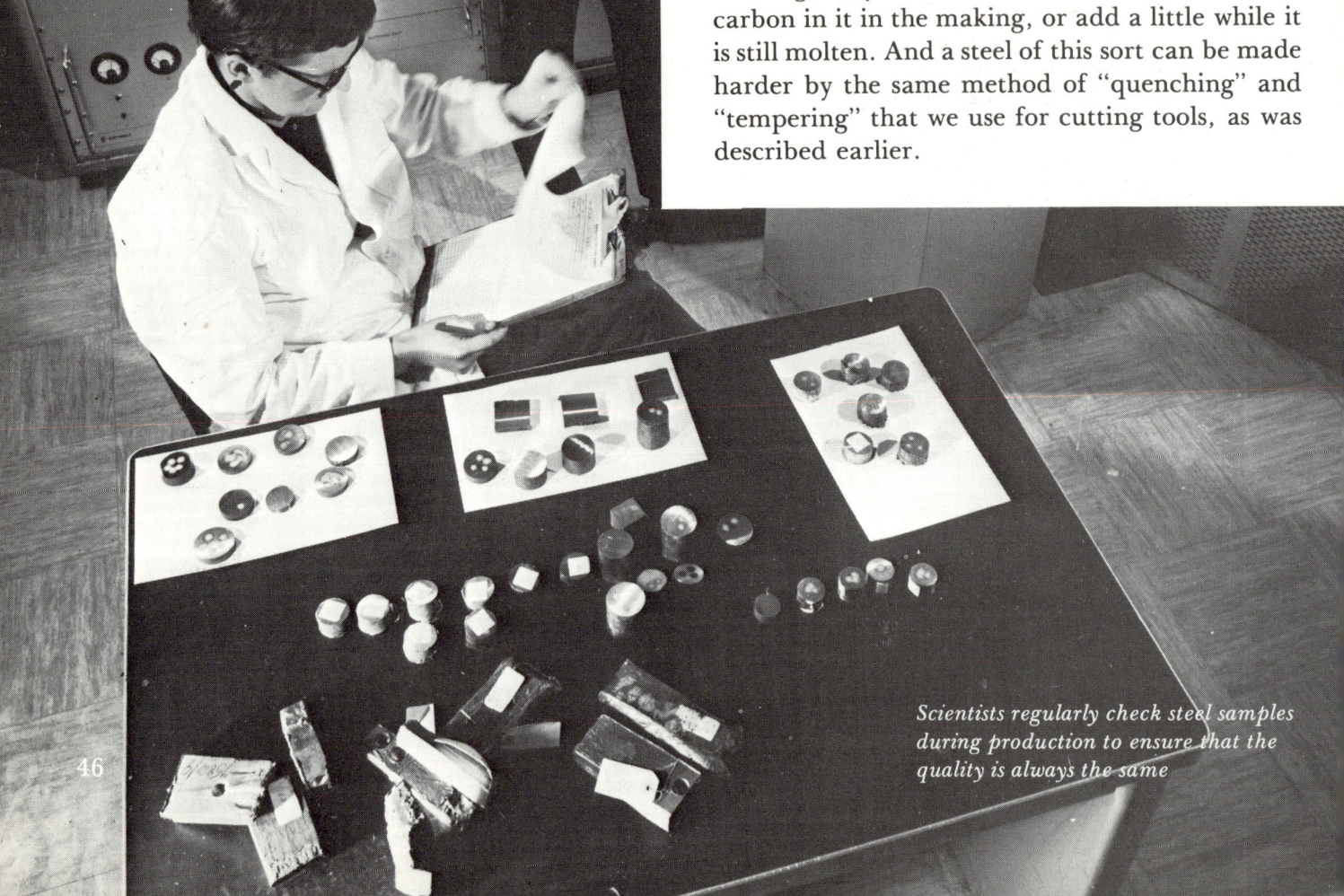

Scientists regularly check steel samples during production to ensure that the quality is always the same

Mild steel is strong and ideally suited for pipelines (above) and electricity pylons (left) . . .

. . . but the gearbox (below) — which must withstand constant friction — has parts made of sixteen different alloy steels

47

The cutting tool on this Mikron gear cutting machine is made of a hard alloy steel which can accurately cut the stainless steel gear teeth

48

Alloy steels

We can also add other metals to our steel, while it is still liquid in the ladle. For instance, nickel and chromium—which are used to give shiny coatings to things like car bumpers—can also be *dissolved* in iron to increase its strength. Manganese, molybdenum and silicon are also added. Manganese, although its name does not end in "um", is a metal, but silicon is not truly one although it behaves very like a metal when it comes to dissolving it in steel. These things, in amounts of up to only two or three per cent, turn our steels into what are called "alloy steels". With these steels we can make stronger and lighter parts than if we used mild steel.

If these steels are strong and tough, what can we use to cut them with? All the parts for machinery must be shaped very accurately, and we need a great number of parts all exactly the same size. If cutting tools were to wear out during the making of a long run of parts, the parts would be getting bigger and bigger and would no longer fit the original engine.

So we need very hard materials for cutting steel, and we make these of alloy steels. The metals that make steel hard are tungsten, vanadium and—again—chromium. They are quite hard in themselves and can harden steel to such a state that a tool still keeps its edge when it is nearly red-hot. Cutting can be very fast too, so we call steels of this kind "high-speed" steels.

Above *Precision cutting with high-speed alloy tools is vital for engine block boring*

Above *Toolmaker working on a press tool die which will stamp out the same-sized car body part over and over again*

49

Stainless steels

We have seen that ordinary steel—mild steel—can be protected against the weather, or sea water, or fumes, by coating it with something, such as another metal, or plastic, or paint. But you couldn't cook food in a saucepan made of galvanized iron, because the zinc would dissolve off and poison you. This wouldn't happen with tin, but tin is rather too expensive for this use. Plastic, as you can see, would probably melt, and you can imagine what paint would do. But there are steels which will stand up to any domestic cooking, to commercial food preparation, and to the making of fierce chemicals as well. They resist all these things without any coatings, and we call them stainless, or corrosion-resisting, steels. What makes them so is that they contain two metals we have heard of before—chromium and nickel—which between them may make up a quarter of the steel. Other metals are also added in small amounts, and when nickel became scarce and dear a few years ago, it was found that quite a lot of it could be replaced by manganese.

So, you see, most of the differences between various kinds of steel are due to the different metals we add. A lot of these metals have no particular uses by themselves, and it is only as ingredients of steel that they come into their own.

Left *A stainless steel goblet. It will resist corrosion from the acid in drinks such as wine*

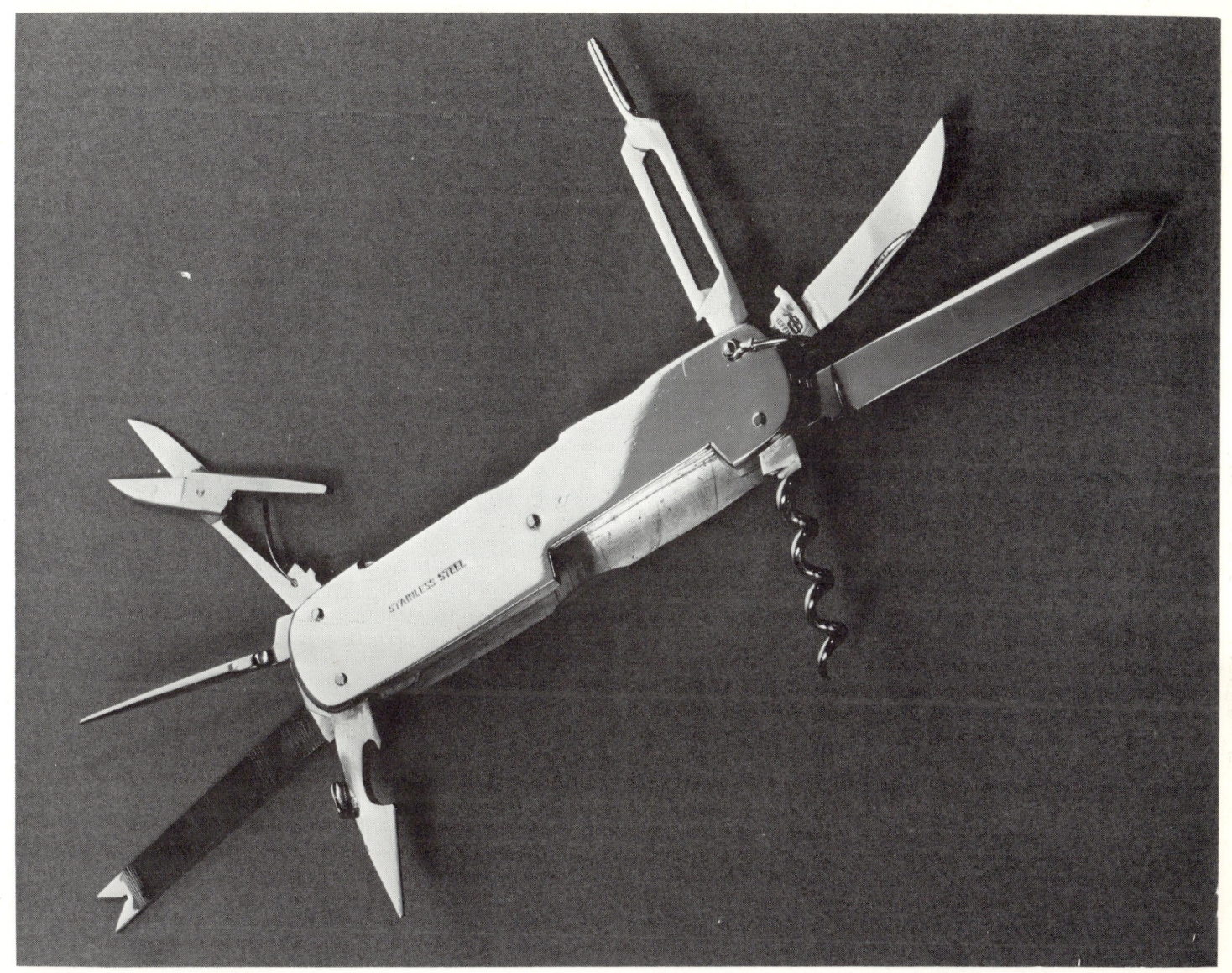

Above *Stainless steel is suitable for making a variety of gadgets—anything from knife blades to tweezers*

Everyday uses of steel

Without steel, farming would still be in the Dark Ages. The wooden ploughshare has given way to steel but the biggest revolution has come with the largely steel-built tractor replacing the horse

To get a lot of things to us, especially farm produce, there is no other way than by road. There is a lot of steel in the roads, both in the reinforced concrete of the road decking itself, and in bridges. The roads would not have been made, through cuttings and over embankments, without the great bulldozers and earth-moving vehicles with their steel scoops, grabs and pushing blades, and their powerful engines.

On the roads there is steel in every vehicle you see: in private cars, in heavy trucks perhaps carrying steel goods themselves, and in car transporters loaded with cars made of steel. Then there are the steel-built carriers of bulk goods transporting bricks for building, oil, chemicals, cement and grain. Steel brings the milk for breakfast from hundreds of miles away, just as it takes the farmer's grain to the miller to end up as corn-flakes.

Steel in farming and road transport

Without steel we should have little food. The plough that broke the plains, the cultivator and the harrow, the mowing-machine and the pitchfork, the reaper-and-binder and the combine-harvester are made of it. So is the silo on the farm, the milking machinery and the milk churn, the barn roof and the pig-pens.

Right *Pressed-steel car bodies on the factory production line*

53

Steel and the railways

Not everything can go by road. Some things are too big for the biggest truck, and too heavy, and some—like iron ore itself—are carried about in such vast quantities that they would block up the roads. Some destinations are just too far even for

and now the wooden sleepers are being replaced by steel. Steam locomotives, with their big steel boilers and their flashing connecting rods, have almost disappeared, but the modern diesels and electrics are made of steel of many kinds, and the electric trains often get their current from overhead wires slung from steel columns. The old wooden goods-wagons are long gone too, and

long-distance lorry drivers, and some goods would spoil because the journey was too long. So the railways still carry great quantities of goods, and great numbers of people, on journeys long and short.

The rails, as we can all see, are made of steel,

nowadays the ore goes from the ports to the steelworks, and the coal travels from the mines to the power-stations, in steel wagons. Passengers travel in steel coaches too, running on steel wheels, which have brakeblocks that are probably made of cast-iron.

Above *Buffers, chassis, suspension springs, brake blocks and wheels of goods-wagons are all made of cast-iron or steel*

Above *Steel-made rail tankers are used to transport oil*

55

Above *The Rohri Channel Bridge over the River Indus. It has the longest steel arch span in Asia*

Below *A fast, refrigerated cargo ship*

Steel in bridges, tunnels and shipping

Roads and railways both have bridges and tunnels. Where they need it, the tunnels will be lined with cast-iron plates and segments, but the gear that makes the tunnels, whether it drives through rock or soft clay, will largely be made of steel. There are still bridges of brick and stone, both on the roads and the railways, but the really big bridges that cross great rivers or link islands to the mainland, or continents to each other, are all of steel. The Bosphorus Bridge that now links Asia to Europe, the Severn Bridge, the Brooklyn Bridge, the Golden Gate Bridge, the Humber Bridge now being built, the Sydney Harbour Bridge, the Kanmon Bridge in Japan and the bridge across the Orinoco in Venezuela, are only a few of the great steel bridges of the world. These are not all of the same design; some are suspended from cables or chains, and some support themselves like a plank laid across a stream, but they all depend on steel.

Under some of these steel bridges go the steel ships: passenger ships, merchant ships, ore carriers, oil tankers, warships and fishing trawlers. All have steel hulls, masts and rigging and, it goes without saying, steel in their engines. And all are carrying things essential to our daily lives: food, imports of raw materials that our industries cannot do without, or exports of the manufactured goods that we must sell in return.

The Mersey Tunnel, Liverpool, is lined with shaped cast-iron plates

57

Steel and power supplies

The fuel that all ships need, whether they are steamships with turbine engines or motorships, is oil. It takes the biggest ships in the world to move this about, tankers 300 metres (1,000 feet) long. And to get this oil out of the ground we need steel. Wells are drilled with thousands of metres of steel drill-pipe, and the oil and gas they give is pumped through steel pipelines. If a ship is filled with oil through a pipeline, it must be emptied in the same way when it gets to port. And if we go for off-shore oil and gas, as in the North Sea, we need steel for the great rigs that stand on the bottom of the sea. These are far bigger than those used on land, and are strong enough to weather the gales of winter, and keep the workers in safety and comfort.

58 **Above** *The turbine hall in a modern power station*

Above *The huge steel frame for a new offshore oil rig is towed out to sea*

Gas and oil are not the only things that need steel for their production and distribution. Electricity is sent about the country in cables supported by steel pylons, or goes underground in cables armoured in steel wire. Electricity power-stations, whether they use coal, oil or atomic power, all generate steam in steel boilers. This steam drives the turbines which, like fast and powerful waterwheels, turn the dynamos that produce electricity.

Steel is important not only in the distribution of oil, gas and electricity. It also helps to send out entertainment. Indeed, it has been in that business a long time, since the first piano with cast-iron frame and steel strings! Today, it provides the masts for TV and radio transmitters, or the guy ropes for reinforced concrete masts, to stay them against high winds.

Above *An attractively designed radio transmitter mast*

59

Steel substitutes and improvements

Right *Plastic pipes reinforced with glass fibre are now being used to carry water*

Could we do without steel?

More and more steel is being used, every year, everywhere. In fact the weight of steel used per head of population is a good guide to the development of a country. In some places, like the USA and Western Europe, up to three-quarters of a ton may be used for every person every year, and in others, like Africa or India, no more than twenty-three kilos (fifty pounds). Steel production is also a good guide to the general level of prosperity in a country—if steel production drops, it is certain that industry is not too flourishing.

Despite the importance of steel in the economy, it might seem sensible to replace some of this steel by other things, since we can see how it uses up mineral resources. There are many other metals, as we know, and some are lighter than steel, like aluminium; some stronger, like the rare metal zirconium; and many, more corrosion-resistant, like chromium. But many of them are rare, and

all are more difficult to extract from their ores. Aluminium, for example, needs enormous quantities of electricity. Moreover, as we have seen, none of them could be a substitute for steel because none of them has all its properties.

Plastics, which seem to be everywhere, might seem to be a good substitute for steel, and in some respects they are. Car bodies are being made of special plastics, and a lot of car trimmings are no longer made of chromium-plated steel. Plastic

60

But the worst feature of plastics is that most of them are made from chemicals produced from oil. As oil becomes expensive, so do they. No one knows for certain what the reserves of metals and oil, respectively, amount to, so we cannot say which will run out first. But it is certain that we can recycle quite a lot of metals— see *Steel and Natural Resources,* later on—whereas when oil is burnt it is lost for ever. We may have to make a choice in the use of oil, and decide whether to use it as a fuel or as a source of chemicals—and that may mean a reduction in the production and use of plastics.

with the thinnest film of chromium is being used instead. And plastics can be used to make bearings that will run for ever without lubrication, whilst some plastics are very resistant to chemicals. But they have their limits; although you can boil water in beakers of certain plastics, a plastic kettle might cost five times as much as a steel one, and you would have to take great care that it never boiled dry. You could never melt metal in any plastic vessel!

Above *Plastic kitchenware has replaced many things previously made in iron or steel*

61

Could steel be improved?

As with everything else nowadays, it would be better if steel could be made to go further. Then we could use less iron ore, less of the ores of rarer metals, less coke, less oil, and not so many ships and railway wagons for moving them about. Scientists are working to bring this about every day, and because of their work the steels we use today are different from those in use even thirty years ago. Ordinary steels, such as those used in buildings and bridges, are stronger, so that there is less steel for the size than there would have been in the past. This has happened because we have discovered what we can do by just a little more care in all the manufacturing stages. In modern engines, for instance, we now use small quantities of alloying elements to make stronger steels. The effect of this is that a car develops more horse-power for the same weight—and it uses less fuel.

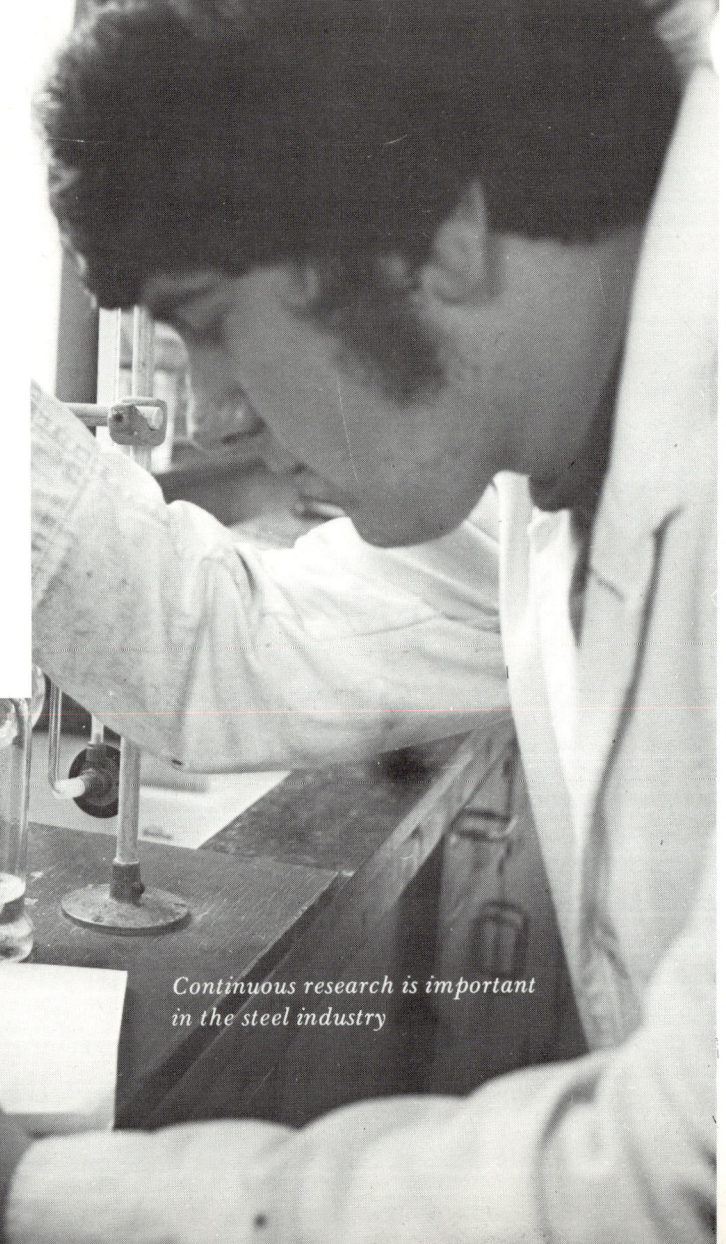

Continuous research is important in the steel industry

62

We have already mentioned that stainless steels, so necessary in the house and in industry, now use less nickel and more of the cheaper metals, yet they are not inferior in their properties. Some steels still need the expensive elements besides nickel, such as chromium, tungsten, molybdenum and vanadium. But we have found out that we can use less if we take care to make the steel to which they are added as pure as possible beforehand.

Vacuum treatment is one way of doing this. The liquid steel is run into a closed vessel, and the air above is sucked out by powerful pumps. As the pressure goes down a kind of boiling takes place, and the gases that are harmful to the steel, especially hydrogen and nitrogen, bubble up and are sucked out by the pumps. These gases have various effects if they are left in; hydrogen causes brittleness, whilst nitrogen may combine with the elements we add. Vacuum treatment is an easy and excellent way of getting rid of them.

Another way of improving steel is by electroslag remelting. In this process, the metal, in the form of bars, is remelted by an electric arc. It is surrounded by special minerals that form a slag, and the final traces of harmful elements, such as sulphur and phosphorus, are removed, as well as the harmful gases.

Lighter and stronger alloy steels are used in modern car engines

Steel as a commodity

Coils of strip steel

64

Buying steel

Who actually buys steel, and where do they go to get it? As steel is a commodity with almost innumerable forms there are many outlets. The simplest forms of steel are sold "over the counter". We go to an ironmonger to buy items such as nails, screws, wire, handtools like saws and chisels, and even small machines. Goods that contain quite a lot of steel, and are quite complicated, also pass from hand to hand in that way; things such as cars, refrigerators and washing machines.

But if you actually want to *make* nails or screws you will need miles of wire, and if you are a washing machine manufacturer you will need square miles of sheet steel. If you are putting up a factory building you will need a lot of beams and girders, and if there is a new branch railway line, someone will have to get hold of a few miles of rails. In many cases, the quantities needed are so large that you would go straight to the steelworks and have them specially made up.

Above *Ancient and modern. An old-style ironmonger's shop* (top) *and* (below) *a modern hardware supermarket*

Other steelworks, though, go on week after week rolling materials in the shapes and sizes that they know are regularly wanted. They roll sheets, bars, rods, light beams, angle-sections for simple building work, and all the products that are used every day by light industrial manufacturers. The people who buy the materials for light industry go to "steel service centres", which are really wholesale merchants carrying a wide range of goods. You might equally call them "steel supermarkets". Here the engineering firm that wants a few tons of round bars of a certain size and a particular composition can buy them and have them cut into convenient lengths. The firm that makes bicycles can buy tubes for the frames, strip to make the wheel rims and wire for the spokes, without "shopping around" the different steelworks that make these things.

Left *Steel plate at the mill*

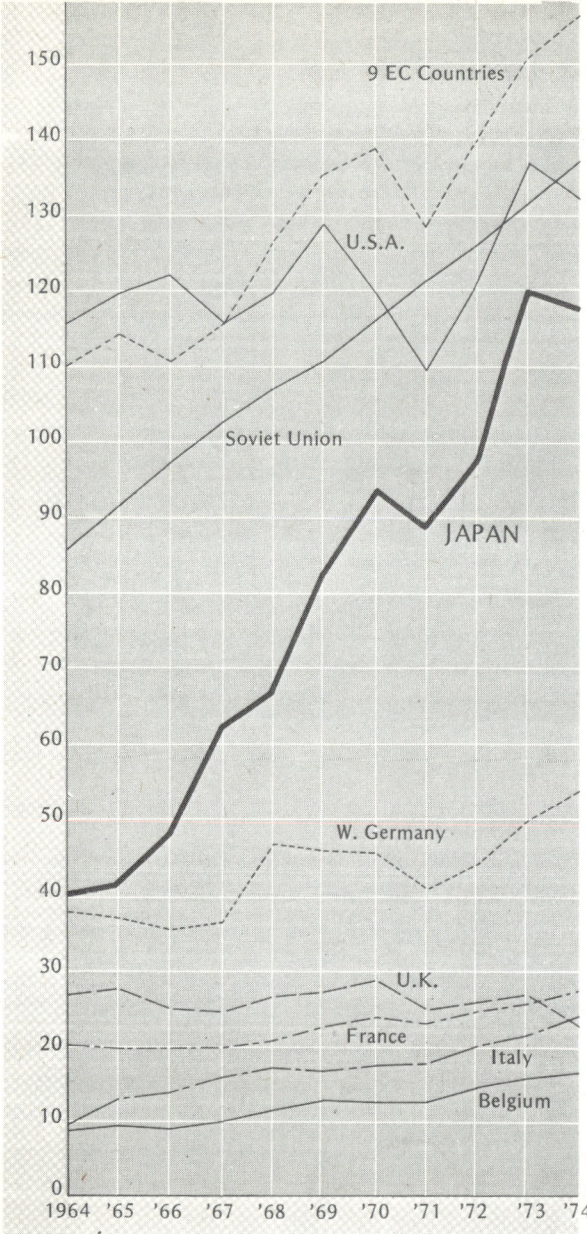

Imports, exports and steel production

There is a world-wide trade in steel in all its forms. Japan, which is the third largest steelmaking country, is the largest exporter of steel. It sends out more steel than the UK produces; most of it goes to developing countries, especially in the Far East, but some does go to America. The United Kingdom both imports and exports steel, and so do most Western countries. Russia, the largest steelmaking country, imports steel in some forms. The reason for this state of affairs is that most countries do not make all the possible qualities or compositions or shapes of steel that they need. Some they do not make because the amount they would require themselves is too small, or because they have not got the necessary raw materials. The result is that one makes what another does not, and there is an interchange.

Although this import and export trade goes on, the big industrial countries make enough for their own general purposes. In 1974, world production was 710.1 million tons. Of this, the USSR, or Soviet Russia, made 136.3 million tons, the USA 132.0 million, and Japan 117.1. The nine countries of the Common Market, the EEC, made more than any single country — 155.7 million tons. The next five countries, China, Poland, Czechoslovakia, Canada and Spain, 80.6 million between them. That leaves 88.4 million tons shared between a dozen or more smaller countries that make steel.

World Steel Imports : 1968, 1973

	European Community (6) : 27 %	(22 % intra-trade, 5 % third countries)
1973	Comecon : 14 %	(8 % intra-trade, 6 % third countries)
	USA : 12 %	

(a) Derived from export statistics   million metric product tons

	1968	1973
USA	15.9	13.4
Fed. Rep. Germany	8.0	10.6
France	5.1	7.8
Italy	2.7	5.0
USSR	2.1	4.8
Netherlands	3.1	4.2
Dem. Rep. Germany	2.4	3.8
China	1.7 (a)	3.7 (a)
Belgium/Luxemburg	1.6	2.9
UK	2.2	2.8
Poland	1.0	2.8
Sweden	1.3	2.1
Switzerland	1.4	2.1
Iran	1.3 (a)	1.9 (a)
Rep. Korea	—	1.9 (a)
Argentina	0.4	1.9
Canada	1.3	1.9
Brazil	0.3	1.7
Denmark	1.2	1.7
Romania	1.1	1.5
Yugoslavia	0.7	1.4
Norway	0.9	1.3
Taiwan	0.6 (a)	1.3 (a)
India	0.5	1.2 (a)
Spain	1.1	1.1
Hungary	0.9	1.1
Other	17.1	25.4
Total	75.9 (a)	111.3 (a)

World Steel Exports : 1968, 1973

	European Community (6) : 45 %	(22 % intra-trade, 23 % third countries)
1973	Japan : 22 %	
	Comecon : 15 %	(8 % intra-trade, 7 % third countries)

million metric product tons

	1968	1973
Japan	12.8	24.8
Fed. Rep. Germany	12.8	17.1
Belgium/Luxemburg	11.2	16.0
France	6.9	8.6
USSR	5.9	7.0
Netherlands	2.6	4.8
UK	4.4	4.2
USA	2.0	3.7
Italy	2.5	3.5
Czechoslovakia	2.2	2.9
Sweden	1.4	1.9
Spain	0.1	1.7
Canada	1.3	1.5
Dem. Rep. Germany	0.5	1.5
Austria	1.4	1.4
Poland	1.4	1.4
Romania	1.0	1.4
Australia	1.0	1.3
Hungary	0.7	1.2
Other	3.8	5.4
Total	75.9	111.3

The Indian Tube Company: a pipecutter at work

Distribution of Steel Production

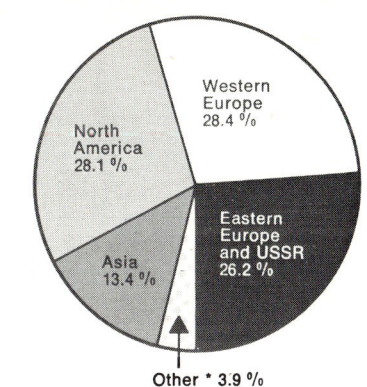

1965
457 million metric tons

* Latin America   1.8 %
Oceania   1.2 %
Africa and Middle East   0.9 %

Other * 3.9 %

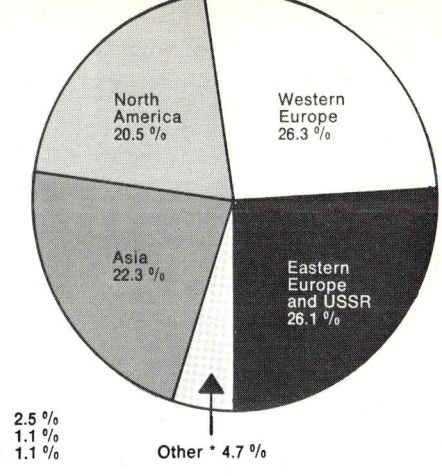

1974
710 million metric tons

* Latin America   2.5 %
Oceania   1.1 %
Africa and Middle East   1.1 %

Other * 4.7 %

Steelmaking in the developing countries

The big industrial countries, the EEC and the Communist countries between them produce over 85 per cent of the world's steel.

Why is the steel industry concentrated in this small number of industrial countries? The reason for this is that ironmaking and steelmaking have become very complex industries. They demand so much, in the way of machinery and technically trained people, that the developing countries have a long way to go to catch up. No one should think that they will never do so; they can and they will.

Many developing countries have already reached the stage where they import semi-finished products from industrialized countries, finishing them in their own factories. And they can produce their own wire, sheets, bars for engineering, small parts and machines, which a few years ago they would have imported or not used at all. To utilize their own natural resources and dispense with unnecessary imports is a step that many countries have taken—the USA being a notable example. The developing countries may, one by one, reach the position where they can do the same.

World Steel Production & Consumption, 1974

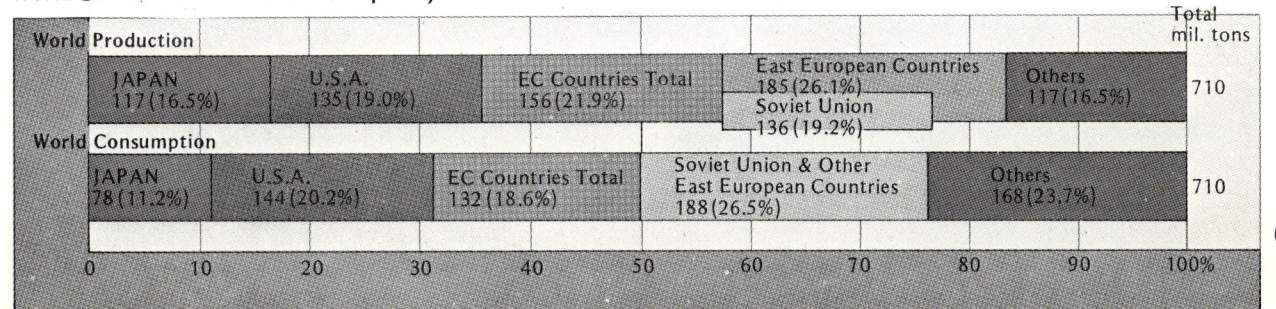

69

Some problems in steelmaking

Could steel be made in other ways?

As we have seen, nearly 90 per cent of the world's steel is made in a very few countries, and they have a minority of the world's population. The rest of the world is dependent on them. It might seem that the balance would be restored if someone could find simpler steelmaking processes. Not going back to the little clay furnaces of primitive man, but forward to a process that would need inexpensive materials and less highly-trained operators. This would make the path to real independence a lot easier.

But it does not yet seem possible, except in rather unusual circumstances, such as those of Mexico. There, a thriving steel industry exists, based on the use of natural gas and a very rich iron ore. But these natural resources seldom occur together, and neither comes out of the ground for the asking. Quite a high degree of skill is required to operate the process.

There are other ideas about, such as the use of the heat from nuclear reactors—atomic power-stations—for the treatment of iron ore to produce steel. But this could only be done in countries that are industrialized already, and it would require a great deal of technical knowledge and skill to bring it into use.

It would be wrong to say that there are no methods other than the present ones just because we have not yet found them. Manufacturing techniques are changing all the time. But any simpler methods of making iron and steel would depend on the same chemical reactions as the present ones do, and these reactions, which are the "laws" of nature, seem to set some limits to our advance.

Above *The Bessemer converter, once used for steelmaking. Bessemers have given way to more efficient modern furnaces*

The processes for turning iron ore (left) *into strip steel* (right) *are both expensive and technically complex*

Teeming white-hot steel—at a temperature of 1600°C—into ingot moulds

72

Steel and the fuel problem

One of the "laws" of nature we have just mentioned seems impossible to get round, and that is that if we want liquid metal which we can run out into moulds or ingots for further use, we must get it very hot indeed. Pure iron melts at 1530°C (2800°F), whereas water boils at 100°C (212°F). The iron that comes from the blast furnace is at about 1300°C (2370°F) because the carbon in it lowers the melting point. But when we have got the carbon out of it again, as we do in all the steelmaking processes, we have to get the metal up to about 1600°C (2910°F) to keep it molten.

Not only do we need heat to keep the metal molten but the heat is also needed to get the chemical reactions going at all. You will remember that the poisonous gas, carbon monoxide, helps to reduce the iron ore to metal. This cannot be produced without burning some kind of fuel; coke or whatever we can substitute for it. Fortunately, before the kind of coal to make the traditional coke has completely run out, we are beginning to find that we can use other kinds, if we treat them specially. We have also found that we can use rather less coke, if we squirt oil into the furnace along with the air. This not only provides heat, but also adds gases containing carbon and hydrogen which help the reactions.

Although, for the blast furnace, some kind of

solid fuel is vital, a good deal of fuel oil has long been used in the iron and steel industry. Fuel oil was used in the open-hearth furnace, which is now of less importance, but it is used in boilers when nothing else is available, and it is absolutely essential for the diesel trucks and locomotives that move things about in steelworks. And of course, all the machinery needs lubricating oil. The industry uses a great deal of oil. And oil is an irreplaceable resource which is all the time becoming scarcer and more expensive.

Steel and natural resources

Like oil, iron ore, too, is irreplaceable; there is so much and no more. Whatever new orefields we find, they have a limit some time. We are learning to use poorer ores and to get more out of rich ones, but there is a constant daily loss of iron in every article that is allowed to rust or is thrown away.

The iron and steel industry itself fortunately wastes very little. Quite a lot of every ingot has to be cut off because it is unsuitable for rolling or forging. But this is never wasted, it goes back to the steel furnace and is remelted. In rolling, too, the ends of a bar or beam or strip may not be quite the right shape; these will be cut off and remelted, too. In every stage of manufacture there is some waste, but it is almost all recovered. For example, when steel is heated for forging or rolling, a thick layer of oxide is formed, called "scale". This falls off, and is collected and returned to the blast furnace.

An essential part of the raw material supply to a steelworks is scrap, both cast-iron and steel; it can all be used. Scrap comes from old machine-parts, from broken-up ships, from steel-framed buildings

Scrap metal recovery

that have been demolished, from car bodies and engine blocks, and from the trimmings and so on that arise in sheetmetal working. Scrap recovery is an industry in itself without which steelmaking would be difficult, and the work of the local junk merchant, or the travelling "rag and bone" man, is only a small part of it. In some countries every old bicycle frame or bedstead will find its way back to the steelworks!

There *are* inescapable losses; slags, which provide useful road-metal—some even provide useful fertilizers because they contain phosphorus which plants need—still contain some iron, and that is lost for ever. But the greatest losses are in food and drink cans that are thrown away, and in junked domestic equipment such as fridges and washing machines. It needs organization to collect the few pounds of steel in each of these; but it all adds up, and one day we shall have to collect it all up, or go without.

Heat recovery and scrap recycling

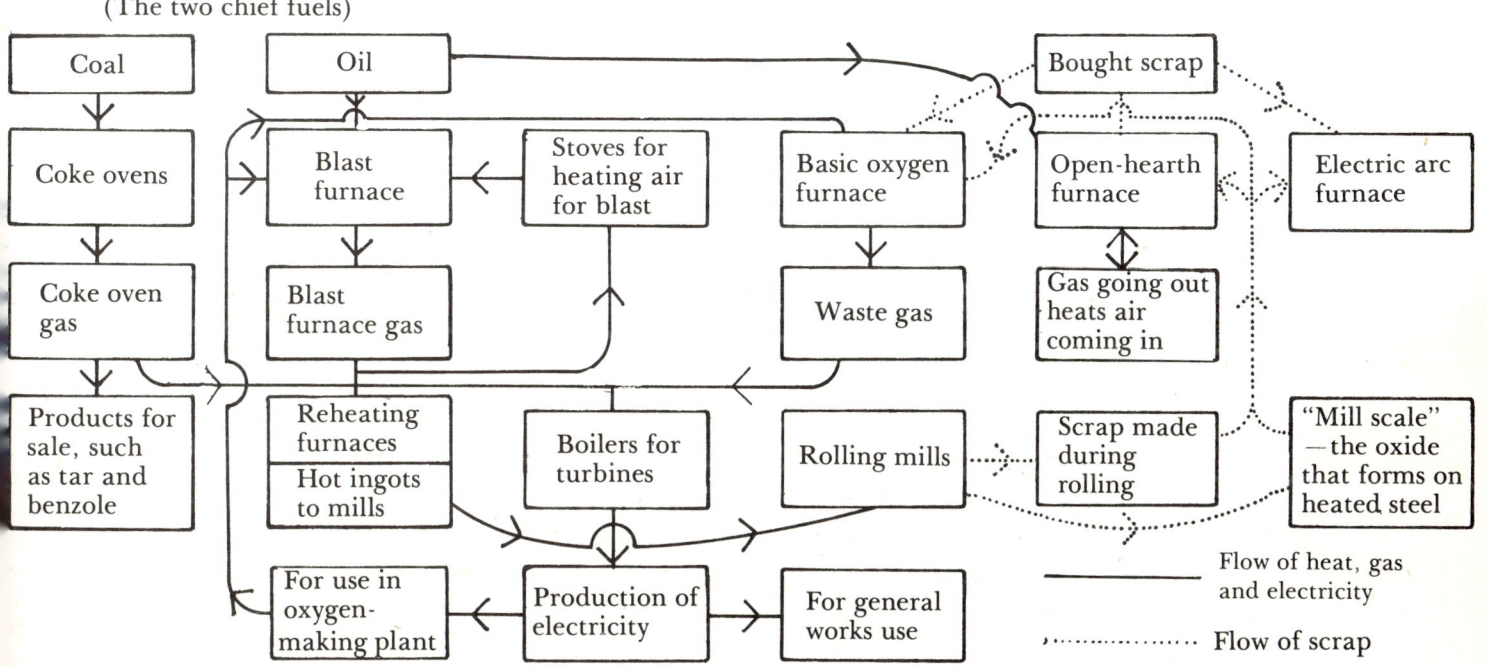

75

Below *Helmet, visor and glasses protect against sparks and glare*

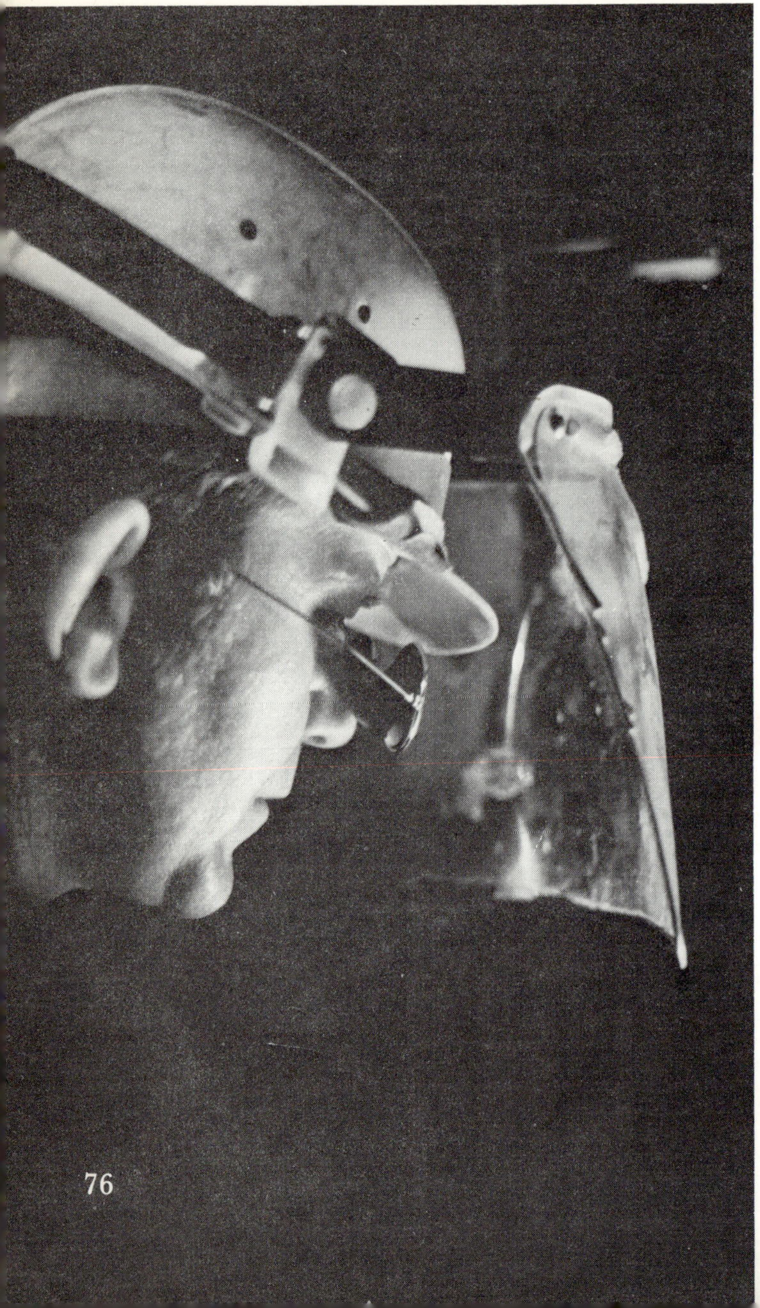

Dangers inside the steelworks

We have considered the place of steel in industry, and its use of our raw materials. It is time, therefore, to think of its effect on our environment, and on the health and safety of the people who make it. We have only to think of a few "industrial" diseases, such as the lung diseases that miners still get, or the poisoning by chemicals that still happens, to wonder if a steel worker is exposed to such things. We know about the death and devastation caused by an explosion in a chemical works making such a harmless thing as nylon, or the damage caused to seashore life and the livelihood of fishermen by a leak of oil from a tanker. We must wonder if a steelworks can injure the men who work there, or menace the people who live round it.

Below *Oxygen lancing in a hail of hot metal*

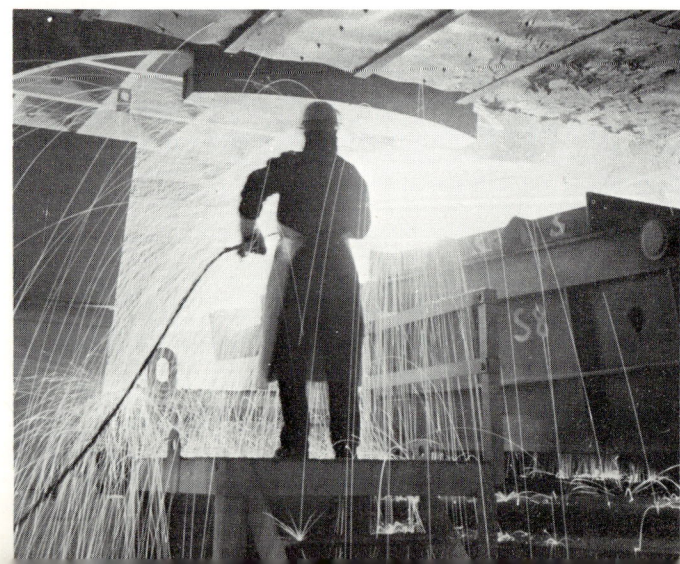

Certainly, hot metal, fumes, smoke, machinery in motion, trucks and locomotives moving about, and loads slung from overhead cranes are all dangerous, and no safety precautions are perfect. But if you went into a steelworks, you would be made to wear a safety helmet; you could have protective boots too, if you needed them. You would see fire-extinguishers and asbestos blankets, and rescue gear for gassy places. You would also notice that all the trucks and locomotives are striped black-and-yellow like wasps to make them clearly visible and you would see plenty of warning notices, both in words and symbols. You might think that this means that there are great dangers. Indeed there are, but it is all these precautions and warnings that keep the accident rate low.

Below *Tapping a blast furnace amidst fumes and hot metal*

Below *An overhead crane carrying coils of strip steel*

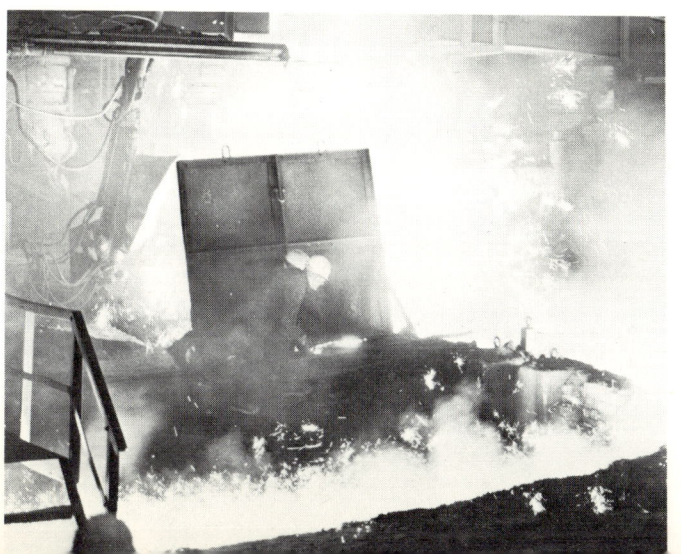

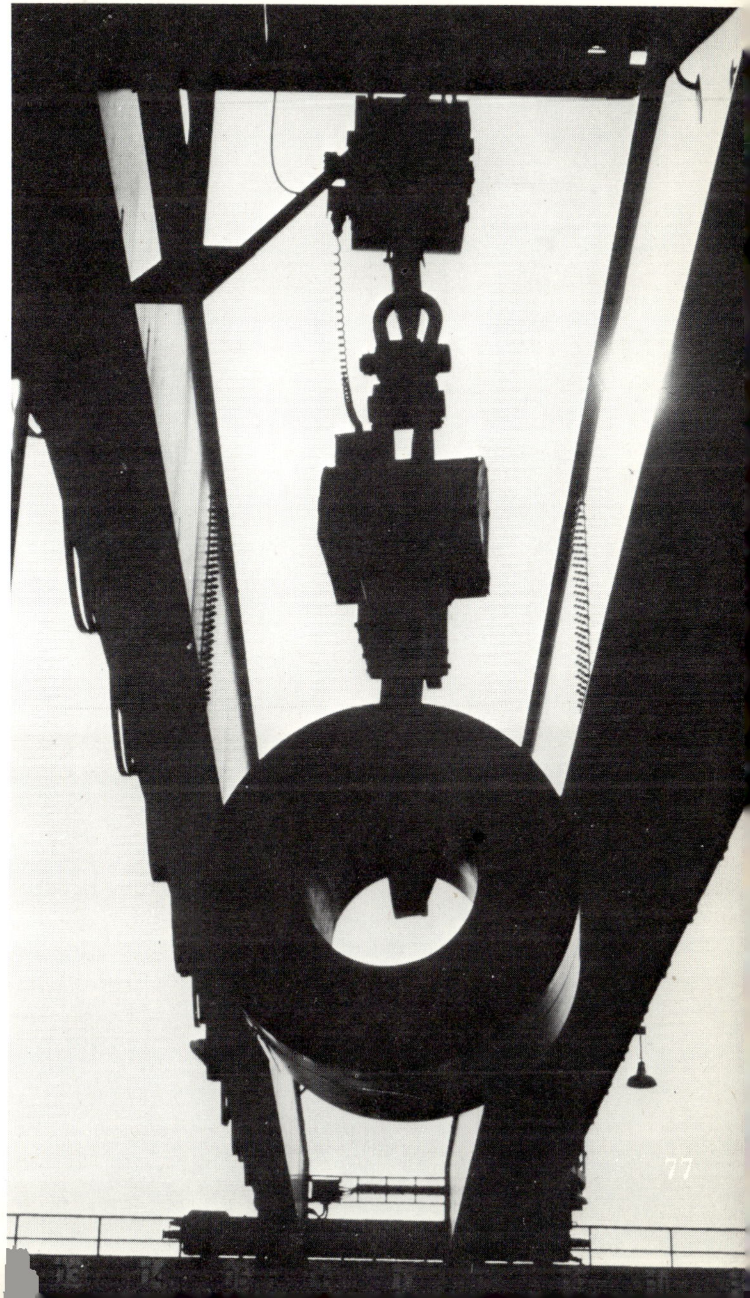

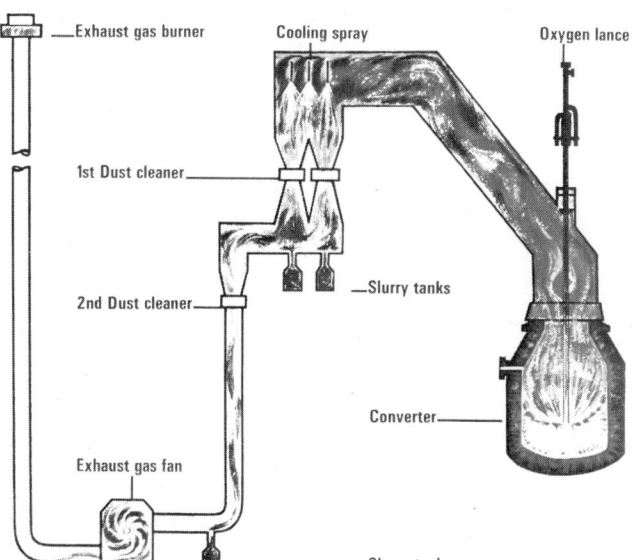

Exhaust gas burner   Cooling spray   Oxygen lance

1st Dust cleaner

2nd Dust cleaner   Slurry tanks

Converter

Exhaust gas fan

Slurry tank

Above *Pollution control in the oxygen furnace:
iron oxide dust is collected as slurry and the
exhaust gas is burnt off or re-used*

Pollution

What is the effect on us outside the steelworks, on
our air and on our water? The iron and steel
industry has never had such a bad effect on the
environment as those industries which burnt raw
coal in factory chimneys or poured waste full of
chemicals into open streams. The industry uses a
great deal of water, and pollutes some of it with oil
and minute particles of scale. This rarely escapes
into the rivers since most industrial countries have
laws to curb this type of pollution. Moreover, in
many places it is absolutely necessary to purify and

Left *The Bad Old Days. Fume emission from the
now obsolete Bessemer converters*

78

recirculate the water, for the equivalent of whole rivers is needed, and there is not that much natural water available.

Steelworks also use enormous quantities of air, but they emit little in the way of harmful gases or fumes. Coke manufacture, when the red-hot coke was cooled with water, used to give off steam and noxious vapours. Local health authorities have made great efforts to prevent this, and elaborate shielding has had to be made. Now that it has been found that the coke can be quenched in its own gas without danger, heat can be recovered and no fumes escape. The gases from the blast furnace are extremely poisonous too, but they are too valuable as a fuel to waste, so they are carefully and harmlessly drawn off the top of the furnace.

Oxygen steelmaking could be a great source of atmospheric pollution, because the fumes emitted are coloured a rich brown with minute particles of iron oxide which can travel a long way. There are laws about this in most countries, and the slightest brown "plume" attracts instant attention from the health authorities. As in blast furnaces, the gas from this process can be used as a fuel, and the iron oxide particles can be recovered and put back into the process.

As we have said, the iron and steel industry is not the worst polluter of our air and water, but many of the ways by which it has avoided—or been made to avoid—pollution have lessons for other industries, by showing that if you are not allowed to throw your waste away you may find a valuable use for it.

Aerial view of the Port Talbot steelworks, Wales

79

Facts and figures

Representing 98 % of World Total
IISI Countries : 67 %

Pig-iron

1965		million metric tons	1974		million metric tons
1.	USA	119.0	1.	USSR	136.3
2.	USSR	91.0	2.	USA	132.0
3.	Japan	41.2	3.	Japan	117.1
4.	Fed. Rep. Germany	36.8	4.	Fed. Rep. Germany	53.2
5.	UK	27.5	5.	France	27.0
6.	France	19.6	6.	China	E 27.0
7.	Italy	12.7	7.	Italy	23.9
8.	China	E 12.0	8.	UK	22.5
9.	Belgium	9.2	9.	Belgium	16.2
10.	Canada	9.1	10.	Poland	14.8
11.	Poland	9.1	11.	Czechoslovakia	13.7
12.	Czechoslovakia	8.6	12.	Canada	13.6
13.	India	6.4	13.	Spain	11.5
14.	Australia	5.6	14.	Romania	8.9
15.	Sweden	4.7	15.	Australia	7.8
16.	Luxemburg	4.6	16.	Brazil	7.6
17.	Dem. Rep. Germany	4.4	17.	India	7.0
18.	Spain	3.5	18.	Luxemburg	6.4
19.	Romania	3.4	19.	Dem. Rep. Germany	6.2
20.	South Africa	3.3	20.	Sweden	6.0
21.	Austria	3.2	21.	South Africa	5.8
22.	Netherlands	3.1	22.	Netherlands	5.8
23.	Brazil	3.0	23.	Mexico	5.1
24.	Hungary	2.5	24.	Austria	4.7
25.	Mexico	2.5	25.	Hungary	3.5
26.	Yugoslavia	1.8	26.	DPR Korea	E 3.2
27.	Argentina	1.4	27.	Yugoslavia	2.8
28.	DPR Korea	E 1.2	28.	Argentina	2.4
29.	Norway	0.7	29.	Bulgaria	2.3
30.	Venezuela	0.6	30.	Rep. Korea	2.0
Total 30 countries		451.7	Total 30 countries		696.3
% World Total		98.8	% World Total		98.1

Per Capita, Apparent Steel Consumption, 1964 to 1973

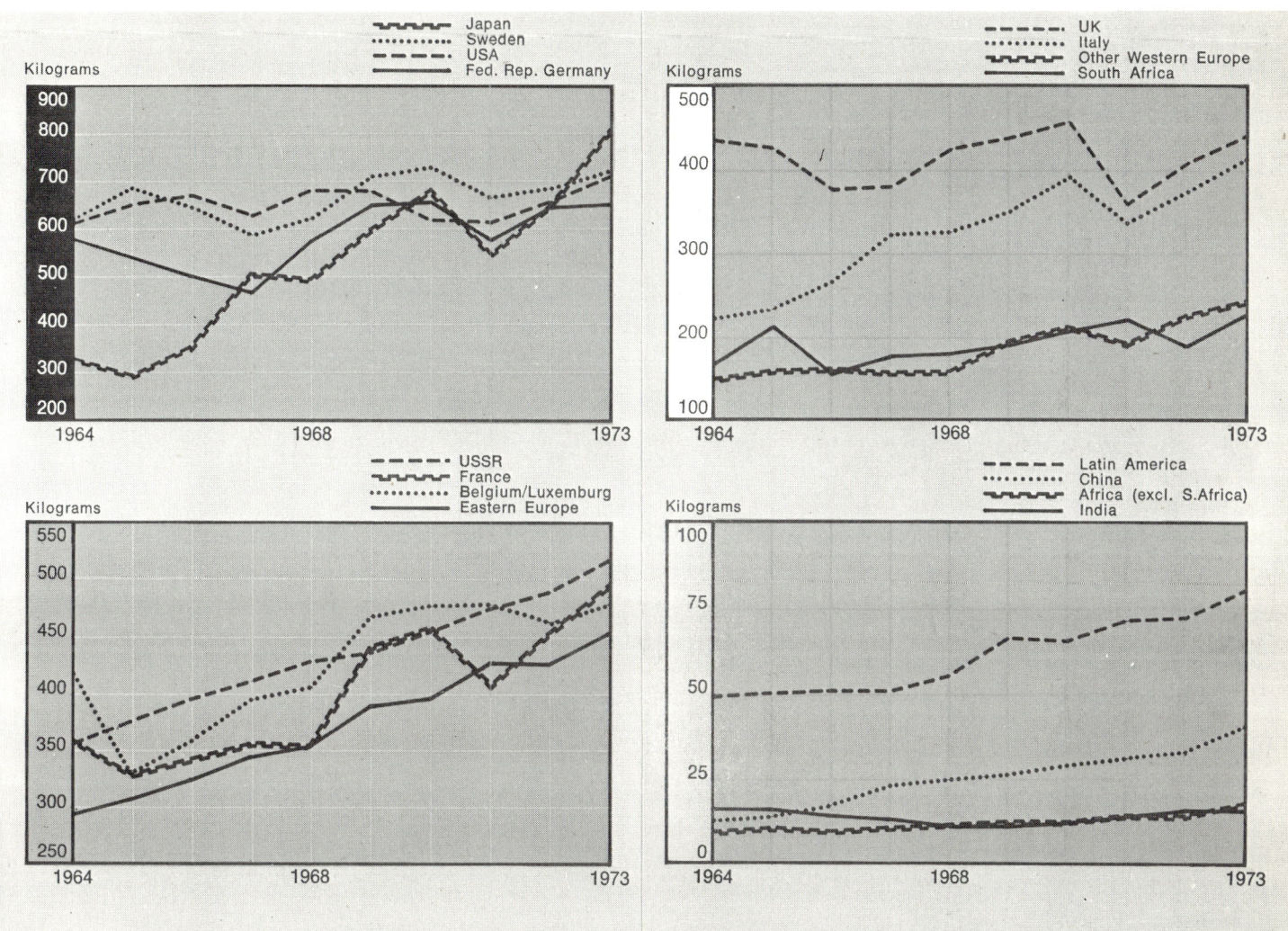

Iron and steelmaking: from raw materials to finished products

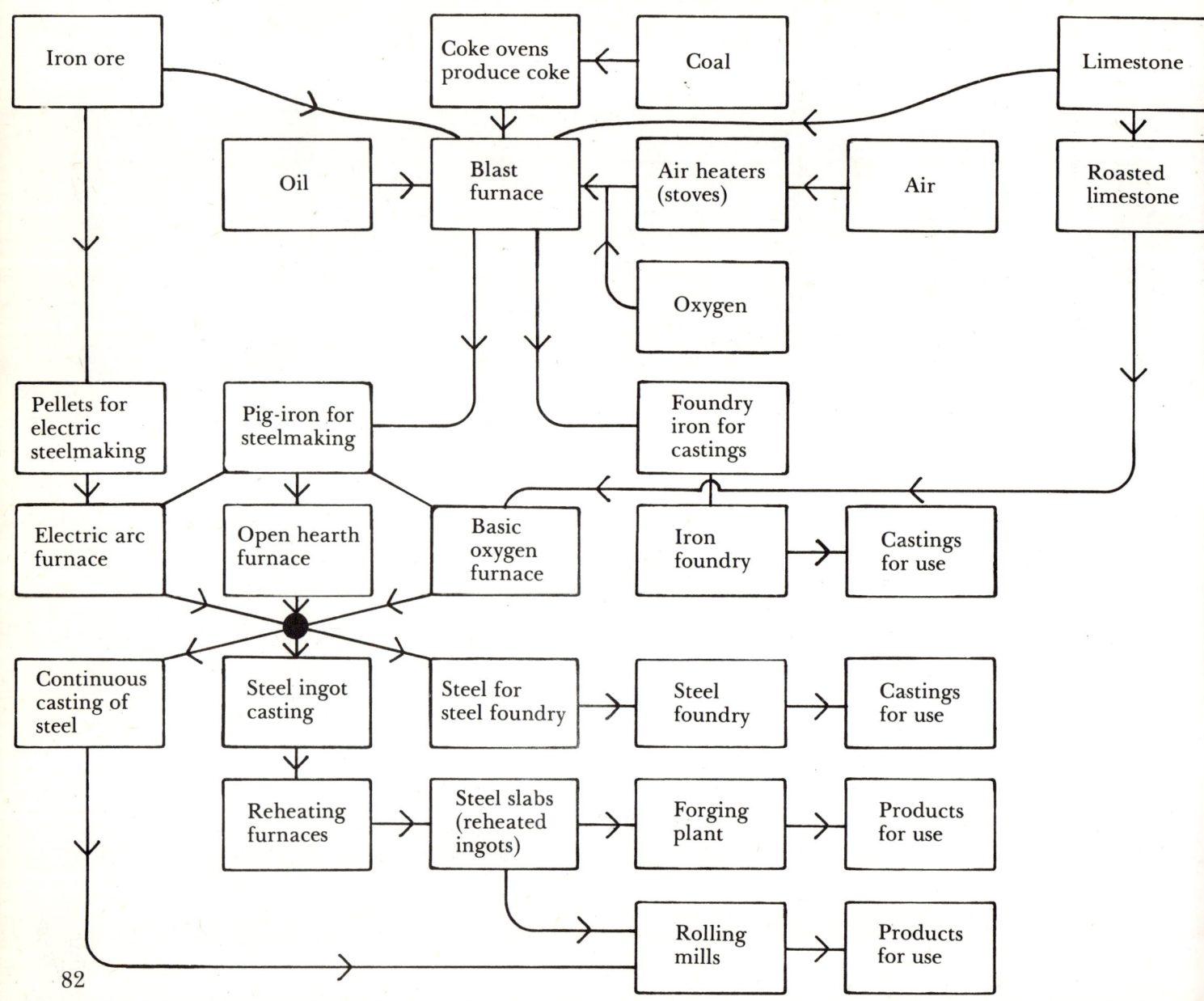

Kinds of steel

General name	Main ingredients besides iron	Uses
Mild steel	*Carbon, in very small amounts, a little manganese and silicon*	Buildings, bridges, ships, pipes for gases and liquids such as water and oil. In very thin sheet form it is "tinned" and used for cans and other containers.
Low alloy steel	*Carbon, as above, with small amounts of manganese, nickel, molybdenum*	In buildings and bridges where greater strength than mild steel is needed. More corrosion-resistant than mild steel.
Alloy steel	*These will have more carbon, and perhaps 3 to 5% of elements such as nickel, chromium, vanadium, niobium and molybdenum*	Heat-treated to bring out their best qualities, these steels are used for crankshafts, gears, drive shafts, parts of electric motors, pumps and drill-pipe for oil drilling.
Tool steel	*These contain quite large amounts— up to 8 or 10%—of tungsten, vanadium and molybdenum*	Essential for cutting tools used on lathes, drilling machines, planing machines and all machines that must accurately cut and shape metal.
Stainless steel	*These always contain chromium and nickel, at least 18% of one and 8 to 10% of the other. Sometimes they contain molybdenum and some of the nickel may be replaced by manganese. If they have to be welded, either titanium or niobium will be added*	These are used in chemical plant making fierce chemicals such as acids, in domestic cutlery, in decorative work on cars and on some buildings.
Heat-resisting steel	*These are much like stainless steels, with up to 30% each of chromium and nickel*	Furnace parts, such as grates, and conveyors for hot metal, and in chemical plant where there is great heat as well as chemical action.

Glossary

Alloy   An alloy is made up of two or more elements, normally metals, that have been melted together. Alloys are usually harder and have better resistance to corrosion than any of the elements in them. Stainless steel is an alloy of *iron, chromium* and *nickel.*

Aluminium   A very light metal, rather soft. In steelmaking, aluminium is added to molten steel to remove oxygen from it; the aluminium combines with the oxygen to form solid particles which either float to the top, or do little harm if they stay where they are formed.

Annealing   When metals are rolled, or forged, they get harder. To soften them, so that they can be worked again, they are heated to red heat and allowed to cool. This is called annealing.

Blast furnace   This is where iron and steelmaking begin, where the metal *iron* is extracted from iron *ore.* It stands over thirty-five metres high, and iron ore and *coke* are continuously fed into it, while heated air is blown in some way above the bottom. *Pig-iron* and *slag* are produced and flow down to collect in the bottom, called the hearth. The slag floats on top of the iron and is run off separately, whilst the iron is run off to form pig-iron, or collected in ladles for steelmaking.

Cast-iron   When *pig-iron* from the *blast furnace* is remelted the metal can be poured into *moulds* to give all kinds of shapes. Any object made by pouring remelted pig-iron into a special mould is said to be made of cast-iron.

Chromium   Chromium is a steel-grey metal, and you will see plenty of it about as a coating. When used to form an *alloy* it adds hardness to steel and much improves its resistance to corrosion; stainless steels contain a lot of it.

Coke   The essential solid fuel used in *blast furnaces.* Coke comes from coal which has been burned in a carefully controlled fashion to drive off moisture, tar and *sulphur compounds* which are not wanted in the ironmaking process.

Continuous casting   In this process, the molten steel is poured into a water-cooled *mould,* and pulled out, solid, in the shape of the mould as soon as it solidifies. Liquid metal is continuously poured in and solid metal continuously removed; powerful rolls pull it down. There is less scrap in this process than in casting in *ingot* moulds in the ordinary way, and less waste of heat.

Draw   To draw merely means to pull. To make wire thinner, it is pulled through a tapering hole, which is called a die. The process is known as wire-drawing.

Ductile, ductility   Ductile means able to be drawn out into a wire or a thread. Ductile material can be drawn, or rolled, out to great lengths without breaking.

Electroplating   This is a method of getting a thin layer of one metal onto another, using electricity. Electroplating is often used merely to improve the appearance of things. Such coatings can protect against corrosion, as does *chromium* on car trimmings.

Forge   A workshop where hammers and presses are used to shape hot metal.

Galvanizing   This is an old word for *electroplating,* named after an Italian scientist called Galvani. He discovered that the electric batteries which had recently been invented in his time could be used to "plate" one metal on to another. Unfortunately the word became applied to all methods of coating one metal with another and particularly to that of coating steel by dipping it into molten *zinc.* Steel coated in that way, without using an electric current, is known as galvanized steel, and if the zinc is put on by electroplating, we have to speak of "electro-galvanized" steel.

Ingot   An ingot is made by pouring molten metal into a metal *mould.* Ingots are rolled or forged to the shapes required.

Iron   Iron is one of the commonest metals in use but it is mainly used when combined with other metals, or with carbon. By itself, iron is not much used as it is rather soft, and quite *ductile* but not very strong. It is also easily corroded. It is one of the very few metals attracted by a magnet.

Lance   A lance is a water-cooled tube for blowing oxygen into molten steel in the furnace.

Malleability   A property very much like *ductility.* The word "malleable" means "can be hammered", but materials that are malleable can also be rolled or drawn into wire.

Manganese   A metal with no uses of its own but very useful in steel, where it increases the elasticity and toughness. If 12-14 per cent is added to steel, the material is not very hard to begin with, but gets harder the more it is banged about or rubbed against hard materials. This alloy is used for railway points, stone-crushers and bulldozer grabs.

Molybdenum   Molybdenum improves the strength of steel at high temperatures, and reduces brittleness.

Mould   Moulds are the hollow shapes into which metals are poured for shaping. For *ingots,* they are made of *cast-iron* and are thick-walled; they produce square section, or round blocks for rolling or forging. For cast-iron, as for *aluminium* and brass, they are made of special sand.

Nickel   Steels containing nickel do not have to be *quenched* so severely; this reduces risk of cracking. Nickel also goes into stainless steel.

Open-hearth furnace   A type of steelmaking furnace which is now becoming out-of-date. It has a long shallow bath of metal, and gas flames blow along it from each end. These, and the heat reflected from the roof, melt the iron. The hot gas going out is used to heat the air coming in, and this produces a hotter flame.

Ore   Very few metals are found in nature in the metallic state. They are combined with other elements, such as oxygen—forming oxides—or with carbon dioxide and oxygen (carbonates), or sometimes with *sulphur* (making sulphides). All these compounds, when they are found in rocks, are called minerals. If there is enough of the mineral in the rock to make it worthwhile to get the metal out, we call it an ore.

Pig-iron   Iron straight from the *blast furnace* is called pig-iron. It used to be run out into grooves in a bed of sand, which branched out from a main stem and resembled a sow feeding piglets.

Quenching   When hot steel is dipped suddenly into oil or water and kept there while it cools, it is said to be quenched. This makes it very hard. *Tempering* softens it again.

Refractories Used for lining furnaces. They stand great heat without softening, and can resist the effects of molten metals and *slag*. Common refractories are silica, magnesite and dolomite — a natural mixture of magnesite and lime.

Roll Metals are made into sheets, bars, rods and beams, by passing them between two electrically-driven rolls. These *draw* the metal like a wringer or mangle does. Smooth rolls are used for sheets, and rolls with grooves for bars and beams.

Silicon A silvery-white element that looks like a metal but, in fact, it is not. However, it acts like one in steel, adding strength; in *cast-iron* it greatly increases resistance to corrosion by acids. Strong sulphuric acid can be pumped by a pump made of "silicon cast-iron" — few other metals or *alloys* can do this.

Slag Mineral *ores,* from which we extract metals, contain compounds that we do not want. To get rid of them lime is put into the furnace with the ore. The lime — calcium oxide — combines with the unwanted compounds to form a slag which has a much lower melting point than iron, so that it melts first and runs down out of the way. The heavier iron is run out from underneath the slag. Slags are not all wasted; they can be used for road-making and as fertilizers.

Smelting Smelting means getting a metal out of its *ore*. This involves turning the metal compound into the metal itself, and the unnecessary parts of the ore into a liquid *slag* which can be removed separately.

Steel Steel is *iron* with carbon and *alloying* elements, like the metals *manganese, chromium, nickel, molybdenum, vanadium,* and niobium, and semi-metals like *silicon,* and non-metals like boron. By the addition of various of these elements, and by rolling and forging, and by heat treatment and cooling, an immense variety of properties can be produced, making a steel suitable for almost any purpose.

Sulphur In steel, sulphur is unwelcome; it forms a compound with the iron which melts easily. But, like nitrogen, it has a use; if just a little is added to a steel containing a little *manganese,* small particles are formed throughout the mass. When we come to put such a steel on a lathe to turn some off, or to plane it, we find that the chips made break at these particles instead of forming long awkward spirals. We call such steels "free-cutting".

Tempering Tempering means partial softening. When red-hot steel is *quenched* by dipping it into oil or water, it gets very hard and brittle. Heating it again to a lower temperature softens it, but keeps a great deal of the strength produced by quenching.

Tin Not added to steel at all, but widely used to coat it. The steel used to be dipped into molten tin, but nowadays *electroplating* is used.

Tungsten Tungsten is itself a very hard metal with a high melting point. It is used in tool steels. Such steels do not soften easily, so they can cut steel very fast — this produces heat, of course — and remove a lot of metal without losing their edge.

Tuyère The water-cooled copper nozzle through which heated air is blown into the *blast furnace*.

Vanadium Another metal used in tool steels. It improves the strength of steel, and its toughness, and makes it easier to harden by *quenching*.

Zinc A common metal of many uses. Though it has no use *in* steel, it is widely used to coat it and prevent atmospheric corrosion — see *galvanizing*.

Sources of information

Iron and steelworks are not normally open to the public but by writing it may be possible to organize a school trip to see the manufacturing processes actually going on. Failing this, a number of museums present good industrial exhibits. Museums are no longer dry-as-dust collections of relics; they use working models, and dioramas and film-shows. The Science Museum in London has a fine iron-and-steel gallery, and it is more than likely that any town in an iron and steelmaking district will have an exhibit of some kind.

Above *A section of the Iron and Steel Gallery at the London Science Museum*

Books to read

There are not many books, of an up-to-date kind, for young people, but here are some which add something, in various ways, to this one:

Metals in the Service of Man. A. C. Street and W. O. Alexander (5th Edition). 1972, Penguin Books Ltd.
Iron and Steel. W. K. V. Gale. 1969, Longmans Ltd.
The British Iron and Steel Industry. W. K. V. Gale. 1967, David and Charles.

Excellent illustrated booklets on iron and steelmaking are available from the British Steel Corporation.

For more advanced reading:

(Some of these may be out of print, but they should all be obtainable through a library.)

The History of British Steel. John Vaizey. 1974, Weidenfeld and Nicolson.
Mills, Mines and Furnaces. Morgan Rees. 1969, Her Majesty's Stationery Office.
The Black Country Iron Industry. W. K. V. Gale. 1966, The Iron and Steel Institute. (This is certainly out of print.)
A Hundred Years of Metallurgy. W. H. Dennis. 1963, Duckworths.
A History of the British Steel Industry. J. C. Carr and W. Taplin. 1962, Basil Blackwood.
Coal and Steel in Modern Europe. N. J. G. Pounds and W. N. Parker. 1958, Faber and Faber Ltd.
History of the British Iron and Steel Industry, C. 450 BC-1775 AD. H. R. Schubert. 1957, Routledge and Kegan Paul Ltd.
Movement of the British Iron and Steel Industry, 1720-1951. H. S. Roepke. 1956, University of Illinois.
Iron and Steel in the Industrial Revolution. T. S. Ashton. 1924, Manchester University Press.

Index

Picture credits

The authors and publisher wish to thank the following for the illustrations in this book: Appleby Frodingham Steel Company, 64 (right); British Hardware Federation, 65; British Insulated Callender's Cables Ltd., 39; British Leyland Motor Corporation, 47 (bottom), 53 (bottom), 63; The British Petroleum Co. Ltd., 59 (left), 73; British Rail, 23 (top), 54; British Steel Corporation, 1, 2, 7, 12, 13 (left), 14, 15, 16, 18, 19, 21, 22, 23 (bottom), 24, 25, 26 (diagram), 27, 28, 29, 30, 31, 32, 33, 34, 35, 36, 37, 38 (bottom), 40, 41, 42 (left), 44, 46, 50, 51, 52, 53 (top), 57, 59 (right), 62, 64 (left), 67, 70, 71, 72, 74, 76, 77, 78, 79, 80 (photo), endpaper photos; Central Electricity Generating Board, 47 (left), 58 (left); Dorman Long Ltd., 56 (top); Esso Petroleum Co. Ltd., 55 (left); Ford, 49 (left); Foster Brothers, 58 (right); Fothergill and Harvey Ltd., 60; H. J. Heinz Co. Ltd., 45 (bottom); ICI Fibres Ltd., 55 (right); Indian Tube Company, 68; Institute of Geological Science, 10 (left); International Iron and Steel Institute, 67 (tables), 69 (top), 80 & 81 (tables); The Japan Iron and Steel Federation, 26 (photo), 66, 69 (bottom); London Transport Executive, 8; The Peninsular and Oriental Steam Navigation Company, 56 (bottom); Plastic Coatings Ltd., 45 (top); Raleigh Industries Ltd., 9; Sanderson Kayser Ltd., 38 (top), 43, 48; J. P. Saville/Chris Brett, front endpaper, 13 (right); J. P. Saville/Gareth Stevens, 75, 82; The Science Museum, 10 (right), 11, 42 (right), 87; Segas, 20; Shell Photographic Service, 47 (top); Tupperware, 61; Wayland Picture Library, 6, 49 (right).